GERMAN - ENGLISH
MATHEMATICAL
VOCABULARY

UNIVERSITY MATHEMATICAL TEXTS

GENERAL EDITORS

ALEXANDER C. AITKEN, D.Sc., F.R.S.
DANIEL E. RUTHERFORD, D.Sc., Dr. Math.

GERMAN-ENGLISH MATHEMATICAL VOCABULARY

BY

SHEILA MACINTYRE

M.A. (Edin.), B.A. (Cantab.), Ph.D. (Aberdeen)

Lecturer in Mathematics at Aberdeen University

AND

EDITH WITTE

M.A. (Aberdeen)

Formerly Assistant in German at Aberdeen University

With a Grammatical Sketch by

Lilias W. Brebner, m.a. (Aberdeen)

Assistant in German at Aberdeen University

OLIVER AND BOYD

EDINBURGH AND LONDON

NEW YORK: INTERSCIENCE PUBLISHERS, INC.

FIRST PUBLISHED · · 1956

PRINTED AND PUBLISHED IN GREAT BRITAIN BY
OLIVER AND BOYD LTD., EDINBURGH

PREFACE

THIS book is designed to help English-speaking mathematicians to read German. The German mathematician wishing to speak or write in English will require more guidance in the choice of the appropriate English equivalent.

The vocabulary covers a fairly wide field in pure mathematics, but applied mathematics, statistics and mathematical logic are not included.

We have aimed at brevity and thus all compound words are omitted if the meaning is clear from the component parts. Thus words such as **Hauptidealsatz**, *principal ideal theorem*, and **Teilbarkeitseigenschaft**, *divisibility property*, are not to be found in the list. Archaic or obsolete words are also in general omitted, as are words which are very nearly the same as the English equivalent (e.g. **Projektion, Tangente, Isomorphismus**).

The formation of different words from one stem is explained in Section VI of the grammatical sketch, and in the vocabulary we give in general only one word of each stem. Thus we include **auflösen**, *to solve*, but not **auflösbar**, *soluble*, **Auflösung**, *solution*, or **Auflösbarkeit**, *solubility*. In this we have not been entirely consistent, but have varied our practice slightly when we felt that this was desirable.

In the case of a word which may serve either as an adjective or adverb, it is translated as an adjective only. Thus **gleichmässig** is given as *uniform*, but not as *uniformly*.

Integers (**zwei, fünfzehn**, etc.) are not included in the list, as these are given in a separate table in Section VIII of the grammatical sketch.

In order to reduce the use of an ordinary dictionary to the minimum, some words have been included (such as

PREFACE

ander, mit, nicht) which, although not mathematical terms, are encountered frequently in mathematical works.

In compiling the vocabulary, we have relied for the most part on earlier dictionaries, translations of standard textbooks and the advice of experts in some of the fields covered. In particular, we are extremely grateful to Dr Hanna Neumann and also to Dr L. S. Goddard, Dr H. B. Griffiths, Professor H. S. Ruse and Dr R. Cecilia Young, who have advised us on many specific points. They have, however, not seen the complete list, even in their own field. Thus any remaining errors and omissions are the sole responsibility of the authors, who would welcome comments, additions and criticisms.

German writers do not appear to be any more consistent than their English colleagues in the use of terms. Thus, in some cases, the same words are found to have different meanings—not only in different branches of mathematics but also, regrettably, in a few instances in the same branch. In a few cases, in fact, various bilingual mathematicians (experts in different fields) have given us contradictory advice. A more ambitious dictionary might be able to deal with this situation satisfactorily by including adequate references and by specifying the field in which the words are used. We had to compromise in some cases and hope that the result is not misleading. Occasionally we do specify the branch of mathematics involved.

The grammatical sketch summarises the characteristic features of German syntax, and we hope that it will enable the reader—with the aid of the vocabulary—to understand most mathematical texts in German. It has been divided into sections to facilitate consultation. To take two examples: if the reader is puzzled by the position of the verb in the German text, he should refer to Sections III and IV under the heading " Word-order," or if difficulties arise from the German practice of separating a prefix from the main stem of a verb, he should consult that part of Section X entitled " Inseparable and Separable Verbs."

viii

PREFACE

It is possible to acquire a working knowledge of mathematical German fairly rapidly by reading a German textbook on a familiar topic, of which a translation is available. Among the many texts suitable to use in this way, we might mention two books in the present series, namely *Integration* (**Integralrechnung**) by R. P. Gillespie and *Integration of Ordinary Differential Equations* (**Die Integration gewöhnlicher Differentialgleichungen**) by E. L. Ince. German translations of these (by Hertha McCabe) have been published by A. Francke, A.-G., of Berne, Switzerland. Specimen passages from each of them along with the translations are to be found on pages 90 to 93.

In conclusion we must point out that even if the vocabulary were accurate and complete on the day of publication, this could no longer be the case in, say, twelve months' time in view of the rapid development of many branches of mathematics to-day. We hope, however, that at least we have lightened the work of later dictionary-makers in the same way as the authors of earlier works have lightened ours. In particular we are grateful to F. Müller (**Mathematisches Vokabularium, Französisch–Deutsch,** Paris, 1900) and L. Herland (*Dictionary of Mathematical Sciences*, New York, 1951). We also wish to express our thanks to Dr D. E. Rutherford for much helpful criticism and advice, and to the publishers and printers for the careful and efficient way in which they have prepared the text.

SHEILA MACINTYRE
EDITH WITTE

Aberdeen, April 1956

CONTENTS

Vocabulary

A

ab, off, down, away from, from

abändern (*sep.*), to change, modify, vary

Abbildung *f.*, mapping, transformation, representation

retrahierende Abbildung, retracted mapping, retraction

* **abbrechen** (*sep.*) (**brach ab** ; **abgebrochen**), to terminate, break off, stop short

abelsch, Abelian

aber, but, however, again

* **abfallen** (*sep.*) (**fiel ab** ; **abgefallen**), to decline, slope down, decrease

abflachen (*sep.*), to level, flatten

Abfluchtung *f.*, alignment

abgeschlossen, *see* **abschliessen**

abgesehen von, apart from, without regard to

abgestanden, *see* **abstehen**

abgezogen, *see* **abziehen**

abgrenzen (*sep.*), to fix the limits of, bound, define

Abhandlung *f.*, discussion, treatise

* **abhangen** (*sep.*) (**hing ab** ; **abgehangen**), to depend on, hang down

abhängig (**von**), dependent (on), sloping

* **abklingen** (*sep.*) (**klang ab** ; **abgeklungen**), to die out, fade away

Abkömmling *m.*, derivative (*not in the sense of differential calculus*)

abkürzen (*sep.*), to shorten, reduce, abbreviate

Ablauf *m.*, issue, outcome, course

* **ablaufen** (*sep.*) (**lief ab** ; **abgelaufen**), to pass, run, elapse

ableiten (*sep.*), to differentiate, derive, deduce

Ableitung *f.*, derivative, derived set, derived group, derivation

Ablenkung *f.*, deviation, deflection

Abmessung *f.*, measure, dimension

Abnahme *f.*, decrease

* **abnehmen** (*sep.*) (**nahm ab** ; **abgenommen**), to lessen, diminish, decrease

abplatten (*sep.*), to flatten, smooth

abgeplattetes Rotations-ellipsoid, oblate ellipsoid of revolution

abrechnen (*sep.*), to deduct, subtract, allow

abrollen (*sep.*), to unroll, produce (*e.g. a curve*), roll

abrunden (*sep.*), to round off (*e.g.* $6\frac{1}{4}$ *to* 6)

abschätzen (*sep.*), to evaluate, estimate, approximate

* **abschliessen**(*sep.*)(**schloss ab** ; **abgeschlossen**), to close, conclude, finish

* **abschneiden** (*sep.*)(**schnitt ab** ; **abgeschnitten**), to intercept, cut off

Abschnitt *m.*, segment, section, intercept

Abschnittkoppelung *f.*, coupling of partial sums (*in series*)

abseits, aside, apart

absondern (*sep.*), to distinguish, separate

Abstand *m.*, distance

abstecken (*sep.*), to lay out, set out, mark out

* **abstehen** (*sep.*) (**stand ab** ; **abgestanden**), to be distant (from)

* **absteigen** (*sep.*) (**stieg ab** ; **abgestiegen**), to decrease, descend

* **abstreichen** (*sep.*) (**strich ab** ; **abgestrichen**), to strike off, discard

abstumpfen (*sep.*), to truncate, blunt

abstutzen (*sep.*), to truncate

abteilen (*sep.*), to divide, separate

* **abtragen** (*sep.*) (**trug ab** ; **abgetragen**), to carry away, level

abtrennen (*sep.*), to separate

abwärts, downwards, lower, on the left

abwechselnd, alternate

Abweichung *f.*, distance, aberration, variation, deviation, difference

abwickelbar, developable

abzählbar, denumerable, enumerable, countable

abzählen (*sep.*), to enumerate, count

abzählende Geometrie, enumerative geometry

* **abziehen** (*sep.*) (**zog ab** ; **abgezogen**), to deduct, subtract

Achse *f.*, axis

Achsenkreuz *m.*, axes of coordinates, system of coordinates

Achtel *n.*, eighth part

addieren, to add

adjungiert, dual, reciprocal (*e.g. frame*), adjoint, adjugate (*e.g. determinant*)

Adjunkte *f.*, adjoint, adjugate, transposed matrix of cofactors

Affinität *f.*, affine transformation, affinity

Affinor *m.*, affinor, affine tensor

ähnlich, similar, analogous, like

allein, alone, but

allerdings, to be sure, by all means, certainly

allgemein, general, universal

allgemeinmetrisierbarer Raum, general metrisable topological space

als, then, as, like, since, when, such as, as soon as

alsdann, then

also, therefore, thus, so, so much, so far

alternieren, to alternate

ametrische Gerade, null line, isotropic line

an, at, to, on, by, against, along, near, as far as, till, with, in

anallagmatische Kurve, curve which, by application of circle inversion, transforms into itself

andauernd, continuous, permanent

ander, other, another, else, different

andererseits, anderseits, on the other hand

ändern, to change, alter

andernfalls, otherwise, else

andeuten (*sep.*), to signify, point out, indicate, suggest

Anfang *m.*, beginning, origin

Anfangsbedingung *f.*, initial condition

Anfangspunkt *m.*, origin

Anforderung *f.*, requirement, claim, demand

anführen (*sep.*), to allege, adduce, quote, lead on

Angabe *f.*, statement, assertion

angeben (*sep.*), to declare, estimate

angehören (*sep.*), to belong to

angenähert, approximate

angenommen (dass), assuming (that) (*also see* **annehmen**)

angeordnet, *see* **anordnen**

angewandt, *see* **anwenden**

angezogen, *see* **anziehen**

* **angleichen** (*sep.*) (**glich an**; **angeglichen**), to equate, equalise

* **angreifen** (*sep.*) (**griff an**; **angegriffen**), to take hold of, attack

angrenzen (*sep.*), to be contiguous (to), be adjacent (to)

Angriff *m.*, attack, commencement

Anhang *m.*, appendix, supplement

anhäufen (*sep.*), to accumulate, cluster

anholonom, non-holonomic, anholonomic

Ankathete *f.*, side adjacent (*in a right-angled triangle*)

anknüpfen (*sep.*), to tie, join

* **ankommen** (*sep.*) (**kam an**; **angekommen**), to arrive, depend on

Ankreis *m.*, escribed circle

ankünden (*sep.*), to announce, declare

anlegen (*sep.*), to apply

* **anliegen** (*sep.*) (**lag an**; **angelegen**), to be close to, adjoin

anmerken (*sep.*), to remark, observe

annähern (*sep.*), to approximate, approach, converge to

Annahme *f.*, assumption

* **annehmen** (**nahm an**; **angenommen**), to assume, accept

anordnen (*sep.*), to order, arrange

anpassen (*sep.*), to adjust, fit, adapt

Anreihungsregel *f.*, associative law

Ansatz *m.*, start

anschaulich, clear, intuitive, heuristic

* **anschliessen** (*sep.*) (**schloss an**; **angeschlossen**), to attach, add, relate

Anschluss *m.*, joining, addition, postscript

anschmiegen (*sep.*), to adapt (to), fit (to)

Anschmiegung *f.*, osculation, adaption

ansetzen (*sep.*), to put, arrange

anständige Funktion, well-behaved function

anstatt, instead of, in place of

anstellen (*sep.*), to place, employ, arrange

* **anstossen** (*sep.*)(**stiess an**; **angestossen**), to be adjacent (to)

Anteil *m.*, portion, share

Antwort *f.*, answer

Anwachs *m.*, growth, increase, increment

* **anwenden** (*sep.*) (**wandte an**; **angewandt**), to apply, employ

Anzahl *f.*, number, quantity

anzeigen (*sep.*), to indicate

* **anziehen** (*sep.*) (**zog an**; **angezogen**), to attract, draw on, quote

Äquipollenz *f.*, equipollence

Ar *n.*, area

arbeiten, to work

Arcus *m.*, amplitude, argument

Art *f.*, kind, manner, sort, type, species

Ast *m.*, branch

auch, also, too, even, likewise; ever (*after* **wer, was, welcher, wie,** *etc.*)

auf, on, in, of, at, by, to, for, up to

aufarbeiten (*sep.*), to work up, process

Aufbau *m.*, construction, structure, development

4

aufbauen (*sep.*), to construct, erect, develop

aufbereiten (*sep.*), to programme, prepare for use

aufeinanderfolgend, successive, consecutive

aufeinanderlegen (*sep.*), to superpose, superimpose

auffassen (*sep.*), to conceive, collect

Aufgabe *f.*, task, problem, exercise

aufgegangen, *see* **aufgehen**

* **aufgehen** (*sep.*) (**ging auf**; **aufgegangen**), to be a factor of, divide exactly

aufgehoben, *see* **aufheben**

aufgliedern (*sep.*), to split into parts, decompose

* **aufheben** (*sep.*) (**hob auf**; **aufgehoben**), to cancel, simplify, reduce

aufklären (*sep.*), to clarify, inform

Auflage *f.*, edition

auflegen (*sep.*), to apply, superpose

auflösen (*sep.*), to solve, unravel

aufrechnen (*sep.*), to add, reckon up

* **aufrechterhalten** (*sep.*) (**erhielt aufrecht**; **aufrechterhalten**), to maintain

Aufriss *m.*, elevation, vertical projection

aufrunden (*sep.*), to round off upwards (*e.g.* $6\frac{3}{4}$ *to* 7)

Aufschluss *m.*, elucidation, information

Aufspaltung *f.*, decomposition

aufspannen, to span

* **aufsteigen** (*sep.*) (**stieg auf**; **aufgestiegen**), to ascend

aufstellen (*sep.*), to set up, erect, establish

* **auftragen** (*sep.*) (**trug auf**; **aufgetragen**), to plot, lay off

* **auftreten** (*sep.*) (**trat auf**; **aufgetreten**), to appear, arise

aufwärts, upwards, upper, on the right

* **aufwerfen** (*sep.*) (**warf auf**; **aufgeworfen**), to raise, cast up

aufzählen (*sep.*), to enumerate

aufzeichnen (*sep.*), to draw, trace, graph

augenblicklich, instantaneous

Augenmass *n.*, inspection

aus, out of, from, of, by, for, on, on account of, in, over, out, ended

ausarbeiten (*sep.*), to work out

ausarten (*sep.*), to degenerate

Ausartung *f.*, degenerate form, deterioration

Ausbau *m.*, development

ausdehnen (*sep.*), to extend, expand, dilate

Ausdruck *m.*, expression, term

ausdrücken (*sep.*), to express

ausdrücklich, express

auseinander, asunder, apart, separated

* **ausfallen** (*sep.*) (**fiel aus ; ausgefallen**), to end, result, turn out

ausführen (*sep.*), to perform, carry out

ausführlich, detailed, complete

Ausgang *m.*, start, origin (*not of coordinates*)

Ausgangswahrscheinlichkeit *f.*, *a priori* probability

Ausgangzustand *m.*, initial state

* **ausgehen** (**von**) (*sep.*) (**ging aus ; ausgegangen**), to start (from)

ausgenommen, except

ausgezeichnet, extraordinary, singular, special, distinguished

ausgezogen, *see* **ausziehen**

Ausgleichung *f.*, adjustment, compensation

* **auslaufen** (*sep.*) (**lief aus ; ausgelaufen**), to run, diverge

auslegen (*sep.*), to explain, interpret

Auslese *f.*, selection

* **ausmessen** (*sep.*) (**mass aus ; ausgemessen**), to measure

Ausnahme *f.*, exception

Aussage *f.*, statement, assertion

* **ausschliessen**) (*sep.*) (**schloss aus ; ausgeschlossen**), to reject, exclude

ausschliesslich, exceptional, exclusive

* **ausschneiden** (*sep.*) (**schnitt aus ; ausgeschnitten**), to cut (out, from)

Ausschnitt *m.*, sector, section, cut, slit

aussen, outside, without

Aussenlinie *f.*, contour, boundary

Aussenraum *m.*, exterior (*e.g. of a closed curve*)

Aussenwinkel *m.*, exterior angle (*e.g. of a triangle*)

ausser, besides, except, out of, without, unless

äusser, exterior, outward, outer, contragredient (*e.g. automorphism*)

ausserdem, besides, moreover

aussergewöhnlich, exceptional, extraordinary

ausserhalb, outside, external

ausserordentlich, extraordinary, very unusual

äusserst, extreme, utmost

* **ausspinnen** (*sep.*) (**spann aus ; ausgesponnen**), to spin out, enlarge upon

* **aussprechen** (*sep.*)(**sprach aus** ; **ausgesprochen**), enunciate, pronounce, express
ausspringend, projecting, convex
ausstrahlen (*sep.*), to radiate, emanate, start
* **ausstreichen** (*sep.*) (**strich aus** ; **ausgestrichen**), to cross out, cancel, delete
Austausch *m.*, exchange, interchange, replacement
ausüben (*sep.*), to carry out, practise, exert, exercise
auswählen (*sep.*), to select, choose, sample
Auswahlprinzip *n.*, axiom of choice, Zermelo's axiom
Auswertung *f.*, evaluation
auszeichnen (*sep.*), to distinguish, trace
* **ausziehen** (*sep.*) (**zog aus** ; **ausgezogen**), to extract, (*e.g. a root*), draw in (*e.g. a curve*), make an abstract of
ausgezogene Linie *f.*, unbroken line
Auszug *m.*, excerpt, abstract

B

Bahn *f.*, path, track, orbit, geodesic
bahntreu, with correspondence of paths (geodesics), path-preserving
bald, soon, almost, quickly, easily
Band *n.*, band, strip

Band *m.*, volume (*of a book*)
band, *see* **binden**
Basis *f.*, base, basis
Baum *m.*, tree
beachten, to pay attention to, take into consideration
beantworten, to answer, reply, deal with
Bedeckung *f.*, covering
bedeuten, to mean, denote
Bedeutung *f.*, meaning, significance
bedienen, to serve, fill, do the duty of
bedingen, to stipulate, postulate
bedingt konvergent, conditionally convergent
Bedingung *f.*, condition, limitation, restriction
befreien, to clear
befriedigen, to satisfy
begleiten, to accompany
Begleitmatrix *f.*, companion matrix
begrenzt, bounded, limited
Begrenzung *f.*, boundary, frontier
Begriff *m.*, concept, idea
begriff ein, *see* **einbegreifen**
begründen, to base, found, prove
Begründung *f.*, argument, foundation
Behandlung *f.*, treatment, development
Behauptung *f.*, assertion, statement
* **beheben** (**behob** ; **behoben**), to remove

beherrschen, to rule over, govern

behob, *see* **beheben**

bei, about, among, at, with, by, for, in, under, in case of, near, in connection with, to, on, considering, almost

beide, both, the two

beiderseits, mutually

beiläufig, approximate, incidental

beilegen (*sep.*), to assign

n-Bein *n.*, ennuple, *n*-uple, *n*-ple, *n*-hedral, frame

beinah, beinahe, almost, nearly

Beindarstellung *f.*, representation by means of a frame

Beinkomponente *f.*, ennuple component

beisammen, together

Beispiel *n.*, example

Beiwert *m.*, coefficient

beizeiten, in good time

bejahen, to answer in the affirmative, confirm

bekannt, known

bekanntlich, as is well-known

Beklammerung *f.*, insertion of parentheses

Belegung *f.*, distribution, covering

beliebig, arbitrary, any

bemerken, to observe, remark

benachbart, neighbouring, adjacent

bennant, named

Benennung *f.*, notation, designation

benötigen, to require

benutzen, to utilise, use

beobachten, to observe, notice

bequem, convenient, fitting

beranden, to bound

berandete Fläche, surface with boundary

berechenbar, computable, calculable

berechnen, to compute, calculate, estimate, evaluate

berechtigen, to justify, authorise, entitle to

Bereich *m.*, domain, region

bereits, already

berichten, to inform, arrange

Berichtigung *f.*, correction, adjustment

berücksichtigen, to take into consideration

berühren, to touch

Berührungspunkt *m.*, point of contact

besagen, to say, state, mean, purport

besagt, aforesaid

besass, *see* **besitzen**

* **beschaffen (beschuf ; beschaffen),** to create

beschaffen, to procure

beschaffen, constituted (*also see* **beschaffen** *above*)

beschäftigen, to occupy, employ, keep busy, engage

beschränken, to bound, limit, restrict

* **beschreiben (beschrieb ; beschrieben)**, to trace, describe (*e.g. a circle*)

beschuf, *see* **beschaffen**

beseitigen, to eliminate, remove

* **besitzen (besass ; besessen)**, to possess

besonder, singular, special, particular

besonders, in particular, especially, apart, extraordinarily

Bestand *m.*, permanence, constancy

bestand, *see* **bestehen**

Bestandteil *m.*, component, element

bestätigen, to confirm, establish, ascertain

* **bestehen (bestand ; bestanden)**, to consist, hold, exist

* **bestehen (aus)**, to consist (of)

* **bestehen (mit)**, to be consistent (with)

bestimmen, to fix, determine, define

bestimmt, definite, certain, determined, determinate

Bestimmtheit *f.*, exactitude, determination

Bestimmung *f.*, determination

* **bestreichen (bestrich ; bestrichen)**, to spread over, extend over

Betracht *m.*, respect, consideration, point of view

betrachten, to consider, investigate

Betrag *m.*, amount, total, sum, value

    absoluter Betrag, absolute value, modulus

* **betreffen (betraf ; betroffen)**, to concern

bevor, before

bewandt, circumstanced, conditioned

bewegen, to move

beweglich, mobile, movable, collapsible

Bewegung *f.*, displacement, movement

Beweis *m.*, proof

* **beweisen (bewies ; bewiesen)**, to prove

beweiten, to extend

Bewertung *f.*, absolute value, valuation, evaluation

bewiesen, *see* **beweisen**

Bezeichnung *f.*, notation, designation, symbol

* **beziehen (bezog ; bezogen)**, to relate, refer (to)

beziehungsweise (bzw.), respectively

bezog, *see* **beziehen**

Bezug *m.*, reference, relation

    in bezug auf, with respect to, with regard to

bezüglich, relative, respective, as to

* **biegen (bog ; gebogen)**, to curve, bend

Bienenwabe *f.*, honeycomb

* **bieten** (bot ; geboten), to offer, bid
Bild *n.*, image, map, graph, picture
bilden, to form, shape, make
* **binden** (band ; gebunden), to bind, tie, constrain
  gebundener Vektor, localised vector, attached vector
binnen, within, inwards
Binom *n.*, binomial
binomisch, binomial
birnenförmig, birnförmig, pear-shaped
bis, up to, down to, to, until
bisher, hitherto
bisherig, hitherto existing
bisweilen, sometimes
Blatt *n.*, sheet, lamina, band
  Descartessches Blatt, folium of Decartes (*i.e. curve whose equation is* $x^3 + y^3 = 3\ axy$)
  Möbius Blatt, Möbius band
* **bleiben** (blieb; geblieben), to remain, be left
bloss, mere, pure
bog, *see* biegen
Bogen *m.*, arc
borgen, to borrow
Böschung *f.*, slope
Böschungslinie *f.*, helix
bot, *see* bieten
brach ab, *see* abbrechen
brachte, *see* bringen
brauchen, to require, want
breit, broad, wide

Breitenkreis *m.*, equatorial circle (*e.g. of a torus*)
Brennfläche *f.*, focal surface
Brennpunkt *m.*, focus
Brennstrahl *m.*, focal ray
Brezel *f.*, pretzel (*in topology*), double torus
* **bringen** (brachte ; gebracht), to bring
Bruch *m.*, fraction
Bruchstrich *m.*, sign of division, fraction bar
Bruchteil *m.*, fraction
Buch *n.*, book
Buchstabe *m.*, letter (*of the alphabet*)
Buchstabenrechnung *f.*, algebra
Bündel *n.*, bundle, sheaf, net, two-parameter family
Büschel *n.*, pencil, one-parameter family

C

For words starting with **C**, *look under* **K** *or* **Z**.

D

da, there, here, in as much as, then, since, because, while, although
dachte, *see* denken
dann, then, thereupon
dann und wann, now and then
darlegen (*sep.*), to lay down, state, demonstrate

darstellen (*sep.*), to describe, represent, display

darstellende Geometrie, descriptive geometry

daselbst, there, in that very place

dass, that

Dauer *f.*, duration, period

dauern, to last, continue

decken, to cover

Deckung *f.*, covering

deduzieren, to deduce

definieren, to define

Dehnung *f.*, stretching, elongation

demgegenüber, opposite this

demgemäss, accordingly, according to that

demnach, then, since, accordingly, therefore

demnächst, thereupon, after this, soon after, shortly

* **denken (dachte; gedacht),** to think, suppose, intend

denn, then, for, than, in that case

dennoch, yet, however

derartig, of that sort

deriviert, derived

derjenige, the one, that

derselbe, the same, the selfsame

Deutung *f.*, interpretation

Dichte, Dichtheit, Dichtigkeit *f.*, density

Dicke *f.*, thickness, width

Diëder *n.*, dihedral

diesbezüglich, referring to this

dieser, this, that

differentiieren, differenzieren, to differentiate

Differenzenverfahren *n.*, method of finite differences

Differenzgruppe *f.*, difference group, factor group (*of an Abelian additive group*)

Ding *n.*, thing, object

diskontinuierlich, disconnected, totally disconnected

doch, yet, though, but, at least, surely

Doppelbruch *m.*, compound fraction

Doppeldeutigkeit *f.*, ambiguity

Doppelgeschlecht *n.*, bigenus

doppeln, to double

Doppelringfläche *f.*, double torus

doppelstetige Abbildung, topological mapping, bicontinuous mapping

Doppelverhältnis *n.*, cross-ratio

dort, there, yonder

dortig, of that place, there

drang durch, *see* **durchdringen**

drehen, to turn, rotate

Drehung *f.*, rotation

Dreibein *n.*, edges of a trihedral

Dreieck *n.*, triangle

Dreieckskoordinaten, trilinear coordinates

Dreiflach *n.*, planes of a trihedral

Dreikant *n.*, trihedral

dünn, thin, rare

durch, through, by, by means of, across, during, owing to

durchaus, throughout, absolutely

* **durchdringen** (**durchdrang** ; **durchdrungen**), to penetrate

* **durchdringen** (*sep.*), (**drang durch** ; **durchgedrungen**), to succeed

durchführen (*sep.*), to accomplish, carry out

* **durchlaufen** (**durchlief** ; **durchlaufen**), to traverse, run through

Durchmesser *m.*, diameter

Durchschnitt *m.*, common part, meet, section, intersection, crosscut

durchsetzen, to cut, intersect

durchsichtig, clear, transparent

* **durchstossen** (**durchstiess** ; **durchstossen**), to cut, intersect

durchweg, throughout, altogether

E

eben, (*adj.*) plane, even, level, (*adv.*) just

Ebene *f.*, plane

Ebenenteil *m.*, plane segment

ebenfalls, likewise

Ebenführung *f.*, linkage for tracing a plane

echt, proper

-eck, -agon

Ecke *f.*, angle, vertex, corner

Eckpunkt *m.*, vertex

Efeulinie *f.*, cissoid

effektiv, effective, actual, real

ehe, before

eichen, to calibrate, standardise

Eichmass *n.*, standard (*e.g. for calibration*)

Eichung *f.*, calibration

Eifläche *f.*, closed convex surface, ovoid

eigen, individual, characteristic, proper, own, peculiar, special

eigenartig, peculiar

Eigenschaft *f.*, property, characteristic

eigentlich, proper, intrinsic

Eigentum *n.*, property

eigentümlich, original, characteristic, proper

Eigenwert *m.*, eigenvalue, latent root

eignen, to be adapted, be suited

Eikörper *m.*, oval-shaped solid

Eilinie *f.*, oval

einander, each other, one another

einartig, singleprimed, monotypic

* **einbegreifen** (*sep.*) (**begriff ein** ; **einbegriffen**), to involve, include

* **einbeschreiben** (*sep.*) (**beschrieb ein**; **einbeschrieben**), to inscribe (*e.g. in a circle*)

einbetten, to imbed, embed, immerse

einblättrig, simple, one-sheeted

eindeutig, unambiguous, unique, uniform, single-valued

eineindeutige Abbildung, **eineindeutige Zuordnung**, one to one correspondence

einengen (*sep.*), to narrow (down), define closely

Einer *m.*, digit

einfach (**einfacher**; **einfachst**), simple (simpler; simplest)

Einfall *m.*, incidence

einführen (*sep.*), to introduce, set up, establish

Eingang *m.*, entrance, entry, introduction

eingebildet, imaginary

eingeschaltet, intercalary

eingeschlossen, *see* **einschliessen**

eingipfelig, unimodal

Einheit *f.*, units, unit, identity

Einheitselement *n.*, identity

Einheitskreis *m.*, unit circle

einhüllen (*sep.*), to envelop

einige, some, several

einigen, to make one, unite, cause to agree

einklammern (*sep.*), to enclose in parentheses, put in brackets

Einklang *m.*, agreement

einleiten (*sep.*), to introduce

einmal, **einmalig**, once

Einmaleins *n.*, multiplication table

einordnen (*sep.*), to arrange, classify

einpassen (*sep.*), to fit

einprägen (*sep.*), to imprint, impress

einrechnen (*sep.*), to include, count in

einrichten (*sep.*), to arrange, order, adjust

einschalig, of one sheet

einschalten (*sep.*), to insert, interpolate (*in non-mathematical sense*)

Einschaltvorgang *m.*, insertion process

einscharig, singly-ruled, simply-ruled

Einschiebung *f.*, insertion

* **einschliessen** (*sep.*) (**schloss ein**; **eingeschlossen**), to include, enclose, comprise

Einschränkung *f.*, restriction, limitation

Einselement *n.*, unit element, unit, identity

einsetzen (*sep.*), to insert, substitute, place, set up

einspringend, re-entrant

einstufig, simple, univalent

einteilen (*sep.*), to classify, divide, graduate

einteilig, one part, single

* eintragen (*sep.*) (trug ein ; eingetragen), to plot, enter

* eintreten (*sep.*) (trat ein ; eingetreten), to occur, begin, enter on

Einwand *m.*, objection

einwandfrei, unobjectionable

einwärts, inward(s)

einwertig, single-valued

einzeichnen (*sep.*), to plot, fill in

einzel(n), single, separate, odd, individual

einzig, single, unique

eirund, oval

elementfremd, disjoint

Elle *f.*, ell, yard, cubit

Endfläche *f.*, flat end, base

endgültig, final, definite, definitive

endlich, finite, concluding, last

Endwahrscheinlichkeit *f.*, *a posteriori* probability

eng, close, narrow, select, restricted

entarten, to degenerate, decay

entdecken, to discover

entfernen, to remove, exclude

Entfernung *f.*, separation, distance

entgegen, against, towards, counter

entgegengesetzt, contrary, opposite

* enthalten (enthielt ; enthalten), to hold, contain

entlang, along

* entnehmen (entnahm ; entnommen), to take from, understand from, learn from

* entscheiden (entschied ; entschieden), to decide

* entsprechen (entsprach ; entsprochen), to correspond to

* entstehen (entstand ; entstanden), to arise, originate, be formed, generate, result (from)

entweder, either

entwickeln, to develop, evolve, expand

Ereignis *n.*, event, occurrence

Erfahrung *f.*, experiment

erfahrungsmässig, empirical

erforderlich, required, necessary

erfüllen, to hold true, fulfil, satisfy, accomplish

ergab, *see* ergeben

Ergänzung *f.*, complement, supplement, completion

* ergeben (ergab; ergeben), to yield

* ergeben (*reflex.*), to result, follow

Ergebnis *n.*, result, sequel, sum, product

erhaben, convex (*curve*), reflex (*angle*)

* **erhalten** (**erhielt** ; **erhalten**), to get, preserve, maintain
* **erheben** (**erhob**; **erhoben**), to raise

Erhöhungswinkel *m.*, angle of elevation

Erkenntnis *f.*, knowledge

erklären, to declare, explain, elucidate, define

erlauben, to allow, permit

erläutern, to explain, illustrate

erledigen, to settle

ermesslich, commensurable

Ermitt(e)lung *f.*, evaluation, determination

erniedrigen, to reduce, lower

erörtern, to discuss

errechnen, to compute, determine

erreichen, to attain, reach

errichten, to erect, set up

Ersatz *m.*, equivalent, substitution, replacement

* **erscheinen** (**erschien** ; **erschienen**), to appear, occur

erschöpfen, to exhaust, use up

ersetzen (**durch**), to substitute (for), replace (by)

ersichtlich, evident, obvious

erst, first, firstly, not until, only

erstere, former, first

erstreben, to strive for, aim

erstrecken (*reflex.*), to extend, reach

Erwartung *f.*, expectation

* **erweisen** (**erwies** ; **erwiesen**), to prove

erweitern, to extend, multiply, expand, elaborate

erweiterte Matrix, augmented matrix

Erweiterungskörper *m.*, extension field

erwiesen, *see* **erweisen**

erzeugen, to generate, produce, give rise to

Erzeugende *f.*, generator, generating element

Erzeugnis *n.*, offspring, derivative (*not in the sense of differential calculus*)

* **erzwingen** (**erzwang** ; **erzwungen**), to force, enforce, extort from

erzwungener Krümmungsvektor, normal curvature vector

etwa, perhaps, indeed, nearly, somewhere, in some way

etwaig, possible, eventual

etwas, something, somewhat, some

eventuell, possible

Evolvente *f.*, involute

ewig, perpetual, for ever

Extremale *f.*, extremal, extremal solution

F

-fach, -fold

Faden *m.*, thread, string, fathom

fähig, able, capable (of)

Fahrstrahl *m.*, radius vector

Faktorgruppe *f.*, factor group, quotient group

Faktorzerlegung *f.*, factorisation

Fakultät *f.*, factorial

Fall *m.*, case, event, fall

* **fallen (fiel ; gefallen)**, to drop, decrease

fällen, to bring down, cause to fall, drop (*e.g. a perpendicular*)

falls, in case

falten, to fold

-fältig, -fold

Faltung *f.*, convolution, folding, contraction (*e.g. of tensors*)

Farbe *f.*, colour

färben, to colour

Faser *f.*, fibre, thread

fassen, to contain, comprehend

fast, almost, nearly

Fastkörper *m.*, near-field

Fastperiodischefunktion *f.*, almost periodic function

Fastring *m.*, near-ring

Fehl-, lacking

fehlen, to be deficient, miss, fail, err

Fehler *m.*, error, deviation, lack

Fehlstelle *f.*, gap

Feld *n.*, field (*e.g. in tensors*)

fern (ferner ; fernst), far, (farther, moreover ; farthest)

Ferne *f.*, distance

fertig, ready, finished, complete

fest, constant, fixed, solid

festlegen (*sep.*), to fix, determine

festsetzen (*sep.*), to fix, stipulate

feststellen (*sep.*), to establish, confirm

fiel, *see* **fallen, abfallen**, *etc.*

Fläche *f.*, surface, area

flächengleich, equivalent (in area)

flächenhaftes Gebilde, figure which may be drawn on a surface or plane

Flächeninhalt *m.*, area, surface area

Flächenintegral *n.*, double integral, integral taken over a region in a plane

flächentreu, area-preserving, equivalent (in area)

Flasche *f.*, flask, bottle **Kleinsche Flasche**, Klein bottle

* **flechten (flocht ; geflochten)**, to braid

* **fliessen (floss; geflossen)**, to flow

flocht, *see* **flechten**

floss, *see* **fliessen**

Fluchtlinie *f.*, vanishing line

Fluchtpunkt *m.*, vanishing point

Folge *f.*, sequence, consequence, sequel

folgen, to follow, pursue, continue

folgendermassen, as follows

folgerichtig, logical, consistent, conclusive

folgern, to infer, conclude, deduce

Folgerung *f.*, corollary, inference

Folgesatz *m.*, corollary

folglich, therefore, consequently, then, subsequently, afterwards

Forderung *f.*, postulate, requirement, condition

Form *f.*, form, method of procedure

Formel *f.*, formula

Formierung, Formulierung *f.*, formulation, precise wording

förmlich, formal, express, as it were

Forschung *f.*, investigation

fort, on, away, off, forth, quickly

fortan, henceforth, onward

Fortdauer *f.*, permanence, constancy

Fortführung *f.*, continuation

fortlaufend, continued, continuous

* **fortnehmen** (*sep.*) (**nahm fort; fortgenommen**), to diminish, subtract, deduce

fortpflanzen (*sep.*), to propagate, transmit

*__fortschreiten__ (*sep.*)(**schritt fort; fortgeschritten**), to proceed, progress, improve, move forward

Fortschreitung *f.*, progression

Fortschritt *m.*, progress

Fortsetzung *f.*, continuation, progression

Frage *f.*, question, problem

fragen, to ask

Fragestellung *f.*, formulation of a question

fraglich, in question

frei, free

Freiheitsgrad *m.*, degree of freedom

fremd, foreign, strange, alien, disjoint

früh (früher ; frühst), early, (earlier, former ; earliest)

fugen, to join, fit

fügen, to add, fit, unite, join, direct

führen, to lead, convey, bring

für, for, instead of, for the sake of, against, in return for, as

Fuss *m.*, foot

Fusspunktskurve *f.*, pedal locus, pedal curve, locus of foot of perpendicular from the origin to the tangent

G

gab, *see* **geben**

gäbe, acceptable, customary, current

galoissch, Galois, normal

galt, *see* **gelten**

Gang *m.*, way, method, thread (*of a screw*)

Ganghöhe *f.*, pitch (*of a screw*)

ganz, whole, entire, integral

Ganze *n.*, integer, whole

ganze Funktion, integral function, entire function

ganzzahlige Matrix, matrix whose elements are integers

gar, finished, complete, ready

Gattung *f.*, kind, species, genus

Gebäude *n.*, structure

gebe, acceptable, customary, current (*also see* **geben**)

* **geben (gab ; gegeben),** to give, prove

Gebiet *n.*, domain, region, subject

* **gebieten (gebot ; geboten),** to rule, govern

gebietstreu, neighbourhood-preserving

Gebilde *n.*, figure, diagram, structure (*not algebraic*)

gebogen, *see* **biegen**

gebot, *see* **gebieten**

Gebrauch *m.*, employment, use, way, manner

gebrochen, fractional, broken

gebrochener Linienzug, polygonal line

gebunden, *see* **binden**

gedacht, *see* **denken**

Gedanke *m.*, thought, idea

geeignet, suitable, capable (of)

Gefälle *n.*, slope, gradient

gegen, towards, against, contrary to

Gegenbeispiel *n.*, counter-example, an example to show that a proposition is false

gegeneinander, opposite, mutually, reciprocally

Gegenfusspunktskurve *f.*, pedal curve of the evolute

Gegenkathete *f.*, opposite side (*in a right-angled triangle*)

Gegensatz *m.*, converse proposition

gegenseitig, mutual

Gegenstand *m.*, subject, object, element

Gegenstück *n.*, counterpart, antithesis

Gegenteil *n.*, opposite

gegenüber, opposite

* **gegenüberliegen** (*sep.*) **(lag gegenüber ; gegenübergelegen),** to be opposite

Gegenüberstellung *f.*, comparison, antithesis

gegenwärtig, present, actual, just now

gegenwert, equivalent

Gegenwinkel *m.*, corresponding angle (*in a triangle*)

gegolten, *see* **gelten**

* **gehen (ging ; gegangen),** to go

gehören, to belong to

Gehre *f.*, oblique line, oblique direction, wedge

gekannt, *see* **kennen**

gekonnt, *see* **können**

gelang, *see* **gelingen**

geläufig, ready, familiar, current

gelegen, see **liegen**

Gelenk n., link, hinge

Gelenkmechanismus m., linkage

* **gelingen** (gelang; gelungen), to succeed

* **gelten** (galt; gegolten), to hold true, be valid, apply

gelungen, see **gelingen**

gemäss, according to, in conformity with

gemein, vulgar, ordinary, common

gemeinsam, common, joint, familiar

gemischt, mixed

gemocht, see **mögen**

genannt, see **nennen**

genau, exact, precise

Genauigkeit f., precision, accuracy

geneigt, oblique, inclined

Generalnenner m., common denominator

genommen, see **nehmen**

genug, enough, sufficient

genügen, to be enough, satisfy, be sufficient

Geodäsie f., geodesy, surveying

Geodäte f., geodesic, extremal

geodätisch, geodetisch, geodesic, geodetic

gerade (adj.), even, straight, upright, (adv.), quite, just

Gerade f., straight line

Geradführung f., linkage for tracing a straight line

geradlinig, rectilinear, ruled (e.g. surface)

gerechtfertigt, see **rechtfertigen**

gerichtet, directed, orientated

geringfügig, insignificant, trivial

Gerüst n., scaffolding, structure

gesamt, total, whole

Gesamtheit f., aggregate, totality

Geschlecht n., genus

geschlungen, curved, winding, linked

geschweift, curved

geschwind, quick, speedy

Gesetz n., law, rule

gesetzlich, legitimate, legal

gesetzmässig, legitimate, regular, following a law

gesetzt, supposing (also see **setzen**)

Gesichtspunkt m., point of view, aspect

Gestalt f., shape, form, structure

gestalten, to form, take shape

Gestaltung f., configuration

gestatten, to permit, allow, grant

gestürzt, transposed

getroffen, see **treffen**

gewähren, to guarantee

Gewebe n., textile, web, cells

Gewicht *n.*, weight, importance, gravity

* **gewinnen** (**gewann** ; **gewonnen**), to obtain

gewiss, fixed, certain

gewöhnlich, usual, ordinary

gewölbt, convex

gewonnen, *see* **gewinnen**

geworfen, *see* **werfen**

gewunden, winding, twisting

das Gewünschte *n.*, the desired result

es gibt, there exists

gilt, is valid

giltig, valid, applicable

ging, *see* **gehen, aufgehen,** *etc.*

Gitter *n.*, lattice (*e.g. in number-theory*)

glätten, to smooth

gleich, equal, equivalent, like

gleichartig, homogeneous, of one kind

gleichbedeutend, synonymous, equivalent

gleichlang, equal, of equal length

Gleichlauf *m.*, parallelism

gleichmächtig, equivalent, equal, having the same cardinal number

gleichmässig, uniform

gleichnamig, homonymous

gleichrestig, congruent (*in number-theory*)

gleichschenklig, isosceles

gleichseitig, equilateral

Gleichung *f.*, equation

Gleichverteilung *f.*, uniform distribution, homogeneous distribution

gleichwertig, equivalent

gleichzeitig, simultaneous

* **gleiten** (**glitt** ; **geglitten**), to slide

glich an, *see* **angleichen**

Glied *n.*, member, term, component

gliedweis, term by term

glitt, *see* **gleiten**

Grad *m.*, degree, order

Gratlinie *f.*, edge of regression, cuspidal edge

* **greifen** (**griff** ; **gegriffen**), to grasp, comprehend

Grenze *f.*, boundary, limit

Grenzfall *m.*, limiting case, borderline case

griff, *see* **greifen, angreifen,** *etc.*

gross (**grösser** ; **grösst**), large (larger ; largest, maximal)

Grösse *f.*, variable, amount, magnitude, length, quantity, value

Grössenordnung *f.*, order of magnitude

Grosskreis *m.*, great circle

das Grösste *n.*, maximum

Grund *m.*, ground, reason, cause

grund-, Grund-, fundamental, basic

Grundlage *f.*, foundation, basis

grundlegend, fundamental, basic

Grundsatz *m.*, axiom, principle

grundsätzlich, fundamental, on principle

Grundzahl *f.*, cardinal number, base

Grundzug *m.*, outline, characteristic

Gruppenbild *n.*, colour-group, group diagram

Gruppentafel *f.*, multiplication table

gültig, valid, applicable

H

halb, half, semi-, hemi-

halber, because of, for the sake of, for

Halbgruppe *f.*, semigroup

halbieren, to bisect, divide in two

Halbmesser *n.*, radius

halbstetig, semi-continuous

Hälfte *f.*, half

hälften, to divide into two

handeln, to treat of
  es handelt sich um, it is a question of

* **hangen** (**hing** ; **gehangen**), to depend on, adhere to

hängt ab, *see* **abhangen**

Haufe, Haufen *m.*, heap, great number

häufen, to accumulate

häufig, frequent

Häufungsgrenze *f.*, upper (or lower) limit

Häufungspunkt *m.*, limit-point, point of accumulation

Häufungsstelle *f.*, limit-point, point of accumulation

Häufungswert *m.*, limit-value

haupt-, Haupt-, principal

Hauptdreikant *n.*, principal trihedral, moving trihedral

Hauptlimes *m.*, upper (or lower) limit

hauptsächlich, principal

hebbar, removable

* **heben** (**hob** ; **gehoben**), to cancel, remove

* **heissen** (**hiess** ; **geheissen**), to call, be called

Helligkeit *f.*, brightness, clarity

her, hither, here, near, since, ago

herabsetzen (*sep.*), to reduce

* **heranziehen** (*sep.*) (**zog heran** ; **herangezogen**), to approach, draw on

* **herausfallen** (*sep.*) (**fiel heraus** ; **herausgefallen**), to drop out, be cancelled

Herleitung *f.*, deduction, derivation

herrühren (*sep.*), to originate (in), proceed, flow (from)

Herzlinie *f.*, cardiod (*i.e. curve whose equation is* $r = a\{1 + \cos\theta\}$)

hier, here, present, in this place, as to this

hiernach, according to this

hiesig, in this place

Hilfe *f.*, help

hilfs-, Hilfs-, subsidiary, auxiliary

Hilfssatz *m.*, lemma

hin, hence, that way, thither, towards, on, along, undone

hinblicken (*sep.*), to look towards

hing, *see* **hangen, abhangen,** *etc.*

hinreichend, sufficient

Hinweis *m.*, indication

Hinzufügung *f.*, addition

Hinzunahme *f.*, addition

hob, *see* **heben, aufheben,** *etc.*

hoch (höher ; höchst), high (higher ; highest, maximum), raised to (*e.g. a power*)

hochgestellte Zahl, index (*of a power*)

höchstens, at most

Hoffnung *f.*, hope, expectation

Höhe *f.*, height, elevation, altitude

hohl, concave

Hohlkugel *f.*, spherical surface

Hülfs-, subsidiary, auxiliary

Hülle *f.*, hull, closure, envelope, sheath, shell

Hüllfläche *f.*, envelope (*i.e. enveloping surface*)

Hüllkurve *f.*, envelope

Hundekurve *f.*, curve of pursuit

hyperbolische Spirale, hyperbolic spiral, reciprocal spiral (*i.e. curve whose equation is* $r\theta = c$)

I

identisch, identical, universally valid

immer, always, perpetually, nevertheless, yet

immerhin, always, after all, still, yet

immerwährend, perpetual

immerzu, always, continually forward

imperfekte Menge, set containing no perfect nonempty set

in, in, at, into, within

indem, just now, whilst, in that, since

indes, meantime, whilst, however

ineinander, into one another

*** ineinanderliegen** (*sep.*) **(lag ineinander ; ineinandergelegen),** to be incident

Inhalt *m.*, contents, capacity, area, volume, meaning

inhaltstreu, area-preserving, volume-preserving

inmitten, in the midst

inne, within

innen, within

inner, interior, intrinsic (*e.g. geometry*), inner, cogredient (*e.g. automorphism*)

innerhalb, within, on the inside

insbesondere, especially, in particular

insgemein, in common, usually

insgesamt, all together, in a body

insichdicht, dense in itself

insofern, in so far as, according as

insoweit, in so far as, according as

inständig, instant, earnest

Integretätsbereich m., domain of integrity, integral domain

integrieren, to integrate

interpolieren, to interpolate

invers, inverse, reciprocal

inwärtig, internal, inward

inwendig, interior, inside, inward

inzwischen, meanwhile, however

irgend, some, any, perhaps, about, at all, ever

irrig, erroneous

Irrtum m., error

isoptische Kurve, locus of points from which two tangents to a given curve make a constant angle

J

ja, yes, indeed

je, ever, at a time, each

je nachdem, according as

jeder, each, every, either

jedoch, however, notwithstanding, yet, nevertheless

von jeher, always, from the beginning

jener, that, yon, yonder, that one, the former

jetzt, now, at this instant

just, just, exactly

K

Kalkül m., calculus

Kalotte f., spherical cap

kam an, kam vor, etc., see ankommen, vorkommen, etc.

kann, see können

kannte, see kennen

kanonisch, canonical

Kante f., edge, corner

Kapital n., principal

Kapitel n., chapter

Karte f., card, chart, map

Kästchen n., block, little box

Kathete f., side (e.g. of a triangle)

kaum, hardly, scarcely, with difficulty, but just, just now

Kautschuk m., rubber

Kegel m., cone

Kegelschnitt m., conic section

Kehle f., neck, throat

Kehlpunkt m., point of striction

Kehr-, inverse, reverse

kehren, to turn

Keil m., wedge

kein, not any, no, not one

keinerlei, of no sort, not any

keinerseits, on neither side

keinmal, not once, never

* kennen (kannte; gekannt), to know (through the senses)

kennzeichnen, to mark, characterise

Kennziffer *f.*, characteristic, index (*e.g. of a logarithm*)

Kern *m.*, kernel, heart, nucleus

Kette *f.*, chain

Kettenbruch *m.*, continued fraction

Kettendivision *f.*, continued division

Kettenlinie *f.*, catenary, (*i.e. curve whose equation is* $y = c \cosh x/c$)

Kettenlinie gleichen Widerstandes, catenary of uniform strength, (*i.e. curve whose radius of curvature satisfies* $s = c \cosh s/c$)

Klafter *f.*, fathom

Klammer *f.*, bracket, parenthesis

klang ab, *see* **abklingen**

klappen, to turn over, rotate (through π)

klappsymmetrisch, symmetric about the main diagonal (*e.g. of a matrix*)

klar, clear, evident

Klasseneinteilung *f.*, partition

klein (**kleiner**; **kleinst**), small (smaller, minor; smallest, minimum)

    im kleinen, locally, in the small

Kleinscher (**Schlauch**), Klein (bottle)

Knoten *m.*, knot, node

Knotenpunkt *m.*, node

Knüpfung *f.*, connection, link

Kohärenz *f.*, set of points (*of set in question*) which are not isolated

Kolonne *f.*, column

Komitante *f.*, concomitant, comitant

kompliziert, complicated

konforme Abbildung, conformal transformation

konjugiert, conjugate

* **können** (**konnte**; **gekonnt**), to be able to, know, be permitted

konnte, *see* **können**

konstruieren, to construct

Kopf *m.*, head

Kopfrechnen *n.*, mental arithmetic

koppeln, to couple, unite

    Abschnittkoppelung *f.*, *see* **Abschnitt**

Körper *m.*, field, body, solid

körperlich, solid

Kote *f.*, z-coordinate (*e.g. height in projective geometry*)

Kreis *m.*, circle, circuit

Kreisscheibe *f.*, circular disc

Kreisteilungspolynom *n.*, cyclotomic polynomial

Kreisteilungszahl *f.*, n^{th} root of unity

Kreisverwandtschaft *f.*, homography, circle-preserving transformation

Kreuzhaube *f.*, cross-cap

krumm, curved, twisted, warped

krummes Polyeder, homeomorph of Euclidean polyhedron

krummlinige Koordinaten, curvilinear coordinates

Krümmung *f.,* curvature

kubieren, to find the volume of, to cube

Kubusverdoppelung *f.,* duplication of the cube

Kugel *f.,* sphere

Kugelfunktion *f.,* spherical harmonic

Kugelverwandtschaft *f.,* homography in space

künftig, future, next, henceforth, hereafter

Kunst *f.,* art

künstlich, artificial

kürzen, to shorten, reduce, cancel

L

labil, unstable

lag, *see* **liegen, anliegen,** *etc.*

Lage *f.,* position, situation

Lagerung *f.,* stratification, packing

lang, long

Länge *f.,* length

Längenkreis *m.,* great circle through poles, circle of longitude

längentreu, length-preserving, isometric, equidistant

länglich, oblong, elongated, oval

längs, along

langsam, slow

* **lassen (liess ; gelassen),** to let, leave, grant, allow

Lauf *m.,* course

* **laufen (lief ; gelaufen),** to run

lauten, to purport, run, read

lediglich, only, solely, quite, entirely

leer, empty, null

Lehre *f.,* theory, science, teachings

lehren, to teach, show

Lehrsatz *m.,* lemma, theorem, law

leicht, easy, light

leisten, to fulfil, achieve, perform

leiten, to derive, lead, direct

Leiter *f.,* scale

Leitlinie *f.,* directrix

lernen, to learn

letzt, last

der (die, das) letztere *m.* (*f., n.*), the latter

licht, inner (*e.g. diameter*)

lief, *see* **laufen, ablaufen**

liefern, to give, supply, yield

* **liegen (lag ; gelegen),** to lie, be situated

liegend, horizontal (*also see* **liegen**)

liess, *see* **lassen**

Limes *m.,* limit

Limitierung *f.,* limitation

Lineal *n.,* ruler, guide

Linie *f.,* line, curve

linienflüchtiger Vektor, sliding vector

Linienteil *m.,* line segment

Linienzug *m.*, part of a line
link, left
linksgängig, left-handed
linksgewunden, left-handed
Linkssystem *n.*, left-handed system
Linse *f.*, lens, lentil
Loch *n.*, hole, cavity, gap
logisch, logical
-los, without
löschen, to cancel, obliterate
lösen, to solve
lösender Kern, resolvant kernel
Lösung *f.*, solution
Lot *n.*, perpendicular line
lotrecht, perpendicular, vertical
Loxodrome *f.*, loxodrome, spherical helix
Lücke *f.*, gap, deficiency

M

mächtig, mighty, powerful
Mächtigkeit *f.*, power, cardinal number
Majorante *f.*, majorant, upper bound
Mal *n.*, time
-mal, -malig, times
manch, many a, some, several
mangelhaft, deficient, defective
mannigfaltig, manifold, varied
Mannigfaltigkeit *f.*, manifold, multiplicity, variety

Mantel *m.*, area, sheet
Mass *n.*, measure, magnitude. *Also abbreviation of* **Massstab**
mass, *see* **messen**, **ausmessen**, *etc.*
Massstab *m.*, unit of length, scale
mehr, more, many
mehrdeutig, multivalued, multiform
mehrdimensional, multidimensional, *n*-dimensional
mehrere, several
mehrfach, repeated, multiple, manifold
mehrmehrdeutig, many to many
meinen, to have the opinion, think, give the opinion
meist, most
Menge *f.*, class, manifold, set, collection, aggregate, assemblage, complex, quantity
Merkmal *n.*, characteristic, attribute
merkwürdig, remarkable
* **messen** (**mass**; **gemessen**), to measure
Messkunst *f.*, mensuration
metrisch, metric
metrisierbar, metrisable, metricisable, which can carry a metric
minder, lesser
mindest, least
mindestens, at least
Minimalfolge *f.*, minimising sequence

Minorante *f.*, minorant, lower bound

mischen, to mix

Mischungsregel *f.*, distributive law

misst, *see* **messen**

Missverständnis *n.*, misunderstanding

mit, with, by, likewise, also, simultaneously

miteinander, with one another, together, jointly

mithin, consequently, therefore

Mitte *f.*, middle

mitteilen (*sep.*), to communicate, impart, give

Mittel *n.*, mean, medium

mittel, middle, mean, medium

mittelbar, indirect

   unmittelbar, at once, immediate, direct

Mittellinie *f.*, median

Mittelpunkt *m.*, centre

mittels, by means of

Mittelsenkrechte *f.*, perpendicular bisector

mitten, midway

mittler, middle, more central

mittlere Konvergenz, convergence in the mean

mittlerweile, meanwhile, in the meantime

mitunter, among other things, occasionally

mitwirken (*sep.*), to co-operate, collaborate, contribute towards

* **mögen** (**mochte**; **gemocht**), to be able, be possible (*used as modal auxiliary* may, might, let)

möglich, possible

momentan, instantaneous

Monotonie *f.*, monotonic law

Muster *n.*, pattern, model

mutmassen, to conjecture, presume

Mütze *f.*, cap

N

Nabelpunkt *m.*, umbilical point

nach, after, according to, behind, to, towards, by, at, in, with respect to

nach und nach, gradually, by and by

Nachbar *m.*, neighbour

Nachbarkeit *f.*, neighbourhood

nachdem, after, afterwards, according as, accordingly

nacheinander, successively, in turn

Nachfolger *m.*, successor

nachg(e)rade, by degrees, gradually, at length

nachher, subsequently, after, afterwards

Nachprüfung *f.*, verification, check

Nachschlagetabelle *f.*, reference table

nächst, *see* **nah**

* **nachstehen** (*sep.*) (**stand nach**; **nachgestanden**), to follow

nachträglich, subsequent, supplementary, additional

Nachweis *m.*, demonstration, proof

nah(e) (näher; nächst), near, close, almost (nearer; nearest)

Nähe *f.*, nearness, neighbourhood

nahen, to approach

nähern (*reflex.*), to approach, converge to

Näherung *f.*, approximation

Näherungsbruch *m.*, convergent (*i.e.* convergent fraction)

nahm, *see* **nehmen, abnehmen,** *etc.*

nämlich, namely, to wit, of course, obviously

nannte, *see* **nennen**

natürlich, of course, natural, intrinsic (*e.g.* equations)

natürliche Zahl, positive integer, natural number

neben, adjacent, beside, near, with, besides

neben-, Neben-, secondary, additional, auxiliary

nebenan, close by

nebenbei, along with something else, besides, incidentally

Nebenecke *f.*, diagonal point (*e.g. of a complete quadrangle*)

nebeneinander, side by side

Nebengruppe *f.*, coset

Nebenklasse *f.*, coset

Nebenseite *f.*, diagonal (*e.g. of a complete quadrilateral*)

Nebenwinkel *m.*, adjacent angle

nebst, with, together with, besides

negieren, to deny

* **nehmen (nahm; genommen),** to hold, take, receive

Neigung *f.*, inclination, slope

nein, no

* **nennen (nannte; genannt),** to name, call, designate

Nenner *m.*, denominator

   Generalnenner *m.*, common denominator

Netz *n.*, net

neu, new

nicht, not

nichts, nothing, naught

nie, never

nieder, elementary, low, subordinate

niemals, at no time, never

nimmer, never

nirgendsdicht, nowhere dense

Niveaulinie *f.*, level curve, equipotential line

noch, yet, as yet, in addition, besides, further, still, nor

noch einmal, nochmal, once more, once again, twice

normal, normal, self conjugate, standard

Normalteiler *m.*, self-conjugate subgroup, normal subgroup

normen, to standardise, calibrate

normiert, normed

Normierung *f.,* normalisation, standardisation

nötig, necessary

notwendig, necessary

Null *f.,* zero

Nullkegel *m.,* **nullteiliger Kegel,** isotropic cone, null cone

Nulllösung *f.,* null solution, principal solution, eigenfunction (*e.g. in integral equations*)

Nullmenge *f.,* set of measure zero

Nullstelle *f.,* zero

numerieren, to number

Nummer *f.,* number

Nummerfolge *f.,* numerical order

nun, now, under present circumstances, well, indeed, then

nur, merely, only, a moment ago, but just

nützlich, useful

O

ob, if, whether, over, on, on account of, beyond

oben, above, up, previously
  nach oben, upwards, above (*e.g. in "bounded above"*), on the right, upper

obenan, in the first place

obenauf, above, uppermost

obendrein, over and above

obenein, over and above

obenhin, superficially

ober, upper, high, higher

Oberfläche *f.,* surface, closed surface

Oberflächenintegral *n.,* double integral, integral taken over a region on a surface

oberhalb, above

Oberkörper *m.,* extension field

Obermenge *f.,* set including another set

Oberring *m.,* containing ring, extension of a ring, superring

Oberzahl *f.,* number belonging to the upper class

obgleich, although

obig, above, foregoing, above mentioned

obschon, although

obwohl, although

obzwar, although

oder, or, or else, otherwise

offen, open

offenbar, evident, obvious

offensichtlich, evident, obvious

Öffnung *f.,* aperture

oft, often, frequently

oftmalig, frequent, repeated

ohne, without, except, besides

ordnen, to arrange, order, classify

Ordnung *f.,* order, degree, arrangement

Ordnungsideal *n.*, order ideal
Orientierung *f.*, orientation
Ort *m.*, locus, position, region
Ortsvektor *m.*, position vector

P

Paar *n.*, pair, couple
ein paar, a few
Parkettierungsproblem *n.*, tiling problem
Partialbruchzerlegung *f.*, decomposition into partial fractions
passend, fit, suitable, appropriate
peilen, to take bearings
perfekt, perfect, complete
Pfeil *m.*, arrow
Lebesguescher Pflaster-satz, Lebesgue's covering theorem
Pflasterung *f.*, paving
planmässig, methodical, systematic
Posten *m.*, term, item
Postulat *n.*, postulate, axiom
Potenz *f.*, power
Potenzierung *f.*, raising to a power, involution
Potenzlinie *f.*, radical axis
Potenzpunkt *m.*, radical centre
Potenzreihe *f.*, power series
Praxis *f.*, practice
präzis, precise
prim, prime

Primzahldrilling *m.*, prime triplet
Primzahlzwilling *m.*, prime pair
Probe *f.*, sample, test, check
Projektivität *f.*, projectivity, projective transformation
projizieren, to project
Prüfung *f.*, test, examination
Punkt *m.*, point

Q

Quader *m.*, rectangle
Quadrat *n.*, square
quadratfrei, without a repeated factor, square-free
quadrieren, to square
Quell *m.*, source
Quelle *f.*, source, authority
quellenfrei, solenoidal
quer, cross, transverse, across
Querstrich *m.*, bar

R

Radikal *n.*, root, radical
Radikand *m.*, quantity under the root sign, subradical
radizieren, to extract a root
Rahmen *m.*, frame, framework
Rand *m.*, edge, boundary, frontier
rändern, to edge, border
Randintegral *n.*, contour integral, integral over a boundary
Rang *m.*, rank, genus

* **raten (riet ; geraten),** to guess, conjecture

Rätsel *n.*, puzzle, riddle

Raum *m.*, space, continuum, capacity

Rauminhalt *m.*, volume

Raumintegral *n.*, triple integral

räumlich, solid, in space, cubical

konvexes Raumstück, convex body

Raute *f.*, rhombus

Rechen-, arithmetical

Rechenblatt *n.*, nomogram, calculating sheet, tabulating sheet

Rechenbrett *n.*, abacus

Rechenschieber *m.*, sliderule

Rechentafel *f.*, abacus, nomogram

Rechentisch *m.*, abacus

rechnen, to calculate, count

Rechnung *f.*, calculation, calculus (*in compound words*)

recht, right, right-hand

Rechte *f.*, right (side)

Rechte(r) *m.*, right-angle

rechtfertigen, to justify

Rechtflach *n.*, rectangular parallelopiped

Rechtssystem *n.*, right-handed system

Rede *f.*, speech, report

reell, real

Regel *f.*, rule

Regelfläche *f.*, ruled surface

regelmässig, regular

Reichweite *f.*, range

Reihe *f.*, series, row, rank, line

Reihenfolge *f.*, sequence, order

rein, pure, clean

rektifizierend, rectifying

Relativraum *m.*, subspace

Residuum *n.*, residue

Rest *m.*, residue, difference, remainder

Restklasse *f.*, coset, residue class

Restklassengruppe, *f.*, factor group, residue class group

Restschnitt *m.*, residual section

reziprok, reciprocal

Riccikalkül *m.*, Ricci calculus, tensor calculus, absolute differential calculus

richten, to align, adjust, arrange, orientate

richtig, correct, normal, true

Richtung *f.*, direction, unit vector

Richtungsfeld *n.*, vector field

Richtungskurve *f.*, curve whose arc-length is expressible as a rational function of the coordinates of its end-points

riet, *see* **raten**

Ringfläche *f.*, torus, anchorring

Riss *m.*, projection

roh, crude, rough

Rollkurve *f.*, roulette

Rosenkurve *f.*, rhodonea, curve of the type $r = a \cos n\ \theta$

rot-a, curl-a (*i.e. of a vector* **a**)

Rotationsfläche *f.*, surface of revolution

rück, back

rücken, to move

Rückkehr *f.*, regression, return

Rückkehrkurve *f.*, edge of regression, cuspidal edge

rückläufig, retrograde, recurrent

Rücksicht *f.*, respect, regard, consideration

rückständig, residual

ruhen, to rest

rund, round

S

Sache *f.*, fact, circumstance

sachlich, qualitative, factual, objective

Sachverzeichnis *n.*, index of contents

Saite *f.*, string, chord

Säkulum *n.*, century

sammeln, to collect, gather

sammt, samt, all without exception, together with

Sattelpunkt *m.*, saddlepoint

sättigen, to satisfy, saturate
    gesättigter Index, dummy index, saturated index

Satz *m.*, theorem, proposition, sentence, precept, dogma

Säule *f.*, prism, pillar

schachteln, to nest

Schale *f.*, shell, sheet, bowl

Schar *f.*, family, system, collection, sheaf

scharf (schärfer ; schärfst), sharp (sharper ; sharpest), acute, exact, clear

Schatten *m.*, projection, shadow

schätzen, to estimate

Scheffel *m.*, bushel

* **scheiden (schied ; geschieden)**, to separate, divide, part

scheinbar, apparent

Scheitel *m.*, vertex

Scheitelwinkel *m.*, vertically opposite angle

Schenkel *m.*, leg (*of a compass*), arm (*of an angle*)
    gleichschenkliges Dreieck, isosceles triangle

* **schieben (schob ; geschoben)**, to move, slide

schied, *see* **scheiden**

schief, skew, oblique, inclined

Schiefkörper *m.*, skew field, division ring

schiefwinkliges Dreieck, scalene triangle

* **schlagen (schlug ; geschlagen)**, to describe (*e.g. a circle*)

schlang, *see* **schlingen**

schlängeln (*reflex.*), to twist, wind

Schlauch *m.*, tube, bottle
    Kleinscher Schlauch, Klein bottle

Schleife *f.*, knot, loop, slide

schlicht, simple, univalent, taking no value more than once

* **schliessen** (**schloss**; **geschlossen**), to deduce, conclude, shut, enclose, close, (*also see* **abschliessen**)

schliesslich, final

Schlinge *f.*, loop (*e.g. of a curve*), knot

* **schlingen** (**schlang**; **geschlungen**), to link

Schlitz *m.*, slit

schloss, *see* **schliessen**, **abschliessen**, *etc.*

schlug, *see* **schlagen**

Schluss *m.*, conclusion, end

Schlussweise *f.*, method (*of proof or argument*)

schmal, narrow

schmiegen, to fit tightly, osculate

Schnecke *f.*, limaçon (of Pascal) (*i.e. curve whose equation is* $r = a \cos \theta + b$)

Schneckenhauslinie *f.*, cochleoid

Schneckenlinie *f.*, spiral, helix

* **schneiden** (**schnitt**; **geschnitten**), to cut, intersect, cross

Schneidende *f.*, secant

schnell, quick

Schnitt *m.*, cut, section, intersection, division, separation

schnitt, *see* **schneiden**, **abschneiden**, *etc.*

Schnittpunktsatz *m.*, theorem on incidence

schnüren, to tie up

zusammenschnüren (*sep.*), to shrink round, tie together

schob, *see* **schieben**

schon, already, yet, besides, only, alone, certainly, indeed, after all

schräg, oblique, diagonal, slanting

Schranke *f.*, limit, bound

Schraube *f.*, screw

Schraubenlinie *f.*, helix

Schraubsinn *m.*, screw-sense

Schraubung *f.*, screw displacement

* **schreiben** (**schrieb**; **geschrieben**), to write

Schreibung *f.*, notation

Schreibweise *f.*, expression, notation, symbol

schrieb, *see* **schreiben**, **abschreiben**, *etc.*

Schrift *f.*, writing, work, text

Schritt *m.*, step

schrumpfen, to shrink

Schubfach *n.*, drawer

Schubfachprinzip *n.*, Dirichlet's principle (*viz.* If there are $n+1$ objects in n boxes, there must be at least one box which contains two of the objects)

schwach (**schwächer**; **schwächst**), weak (weaker; weakest)

schwang, *see* **schwingen**

Schwankung *f.*, variation, oscillation, fluctuation

schwer, difficult, heavy

Schwerpunkt *m.*, centre of gravity, centroid

schwierig, difficult

* **schwingen** (**schwang** ; **geschwungen**), oscillate, vibrate, swing

Seelenachse *f.*, skeleton (*e.g. of a torus*)

Sehne *f.*, chord

Sehnen-, inscribed (*e.g. polygon*)

sehr, very, much, greatly

Seifenblase, Seifenhaut *f.*, soapbubble, soapfilm

Seite *f.*, side, page, face

Seitenfläche *f.*, face (*e.g. of a tetrahedron*)

Seitenhalbierende *f.*, median

Seitenriss *m.*, side-view, elevation

seitlich, lateral

Sekans *m.*, secant (*of an angle*)

selbst, self, myself, himself, etc.

selbstverständlich, of course

semikonvergent, semiconvergent, asymptotic

senken, to lower, drop (*e.g. a perpendicular*)

senkrecht, perpendicular, vertical, orthogonal

setzen, to set, put, place, apply

sicher, certain, true, stable, safe

sicherlich, surely, certainly, undoubtedly

sichern, to make sure, guarantee

sichtbar, visible, apparent

Sieb *n.*, sieve

Sinn *m.*, sense, direction, meaning

sinngemäss, significant, appropriate, sensible

sinnvoll, having a meaning, making sense

Sinuslinie *f.*, sine curve

Skala *f.*, scale, graduation

skizzieren, to make a rough draft of, sketch

so, thus, then, so, as, in this degree

so . . . als, as . . . as

so . . . wie, as . . . as

so etwas, such a thing

sofern, so far, as far as, if **insofern**, in as much as

sofort, immediately, forthwith

sogar, even

solch, such

somit, consequently, accordingly, then

sonach, consequently, accordingly, then

sonder, special, separate, without

sonderbar, singular, peculiar, odd

sondern, but

sonst, otherwise, else, besides, in other respects, independently of that, moreover, formerly

34

sosehr, so much, to such a degree, in such a manner

soviel, so much, as much

soweit, so as, according as, as also, as well as

sowohl, as much, as well

Spalte *f.*, column (*e.g. of a matrix*)

spalten, to split, branch off

Spaltung *f.*, process of splitting

spann aus, *see* **ausspinnen**

Spanne *f.*, span, range, interval

Spannweite *f.*, span

spät (später ; spätest), late (later ; latest)

spezial, speziell, special, proper, particular

Sphäre *f.*, sphere

Spiegel *m.*, mirror

spiegelbildliche Symmetrie, bilateral symmetry

spiegeln, to reflect

Spiegelung *f.*, reflection

spielen, to play (*e.g. a rôle*)

Spielraum *m.*, margin, latitude

Spinor *m.*, spinor, spin tensor

spitz, acute

Spitze *f.*, vertex, point, cusp

sprach aus, *see* **aussprechen**

Sprung *m.*, jump, gap, discontinuity

sprunghaft, discontinuous, discrete

Sprungstelle *f.*, jump discontinuity

Sprungweite *f.*, amount of jump or discontinuity

Spur *f.*, trace, spur (*e.g. in matrix theory*)

Stab *m.*, rod, sliding vector

Stammkörper *m.*, stem field

Stand *m.*, position

stand, *see* **stehen, abstehen,** *etc.*

Stange *f.*, rod

stark (stärker ; stärkest), strong (stronger ; strongest), pronounced

starr, stiff, motionless, inflexible, solid

statt, in place (of), instead (of)

Stechzirkel *m.*, pair of dividers

* **stehen (stand ; gestanden),** to stand, remain, be, be upright, be situated

* **steigen (stieg ; gestiegen),** to increase, ascend

steil, steep

Stelle *f.*, place, position, point

stellen, to put, place, set (*e.g. a problem*), put right, regulate

Stellenring *m.*, local ring

Stellung *f.*, position, place

Problemstellung *f.*, statement of the problem, posing of the problem

Stern *m.*, star, asterisk

stetig, continuous

stets, always, steadily

stichhaltig, sound, tenable

stieg, *see* **steigen, absteigen,** *etc.*

stiess an, stiess durch, *etc.,* *see* **anstossen, durchstossen,** *etc.*

Stillstand *m.,* cessation, inactivity

stimmen, to check, add up correctly, accord

Storchschnabel *m.,* pantograph

Störung *f.,* disturbance, interference, perturbation

Strahl *m.,* ray, radius, straight line

Strahlenbüschel *m.,* pencil of rays

streben, to tend (towards), aim (at)

streckbar, rectifiable

Strecke *f.,* line, interval, line-segment

strecken, to stretch
    gestreckter Winkel, straight angle (*i.e.* π)

* **streichen (strich; gestrichen),** to diminish, subtract, delete, strike out, cancel

Streif *m.,* strip, fringe

streng, strict, rigorous, exact, rigid

Strich *m.,* dash, bar, prime, line

strich, *see* **streichen, abstreichen,** *etc.*

stricheln, to mark by a broken line

Struktur *f.,* structure, lattice (*algebraic*)

Stück *n.,* piece, part

stückeln, to fragment, cut into small pieces

Stufe *f.,* degree, step, grade

Stufenwinkel *m.,* corresponding angle (*e.g. of parallel lines with transversal*)

Stumpf *m.,* frustum

stumpf, obtuse

stürzen, to reflect (*e.g. in principal diagonal of matrix*)

Stützebene *f.,* supporting plane, tac-plane

stützen, to support

Stützfunktion *f.,* supporting function

subtrahieren, to subtract

suchen, to seek, look for, require

summierbar, summable

superponieren, to superpose, superimpose

Systembruch *m.,* radix fraction

T

Tafel *f.,* table, projection plane, blackboard

in der Tat, indeed

Tatsache *f.,* property, fact, evidence

tatsächlich, actually

Teil *m.,* part

teil-, Teil-, partial, sub-

teilen, to divide, graduate

Teiler, Theiler *m.,* divisor, factor, subgroup

teilerfremd, having no common divisor, relatively prime

Teilerkettensatz *m.*, divisor chain condition

Teilkörper *m.*, subfield

Teilmenge *f.*, subset, subclass

teilweise, partially, by parts

Tendenz *f.*, tendency, trend

Tetragon *n.*, quadrilateral

Theiler, *see* **Teiler**

tief (tiefer ; tiefst), deep (deeper ; deepest), high

Tiefe *f.*, depth

tilgen, to erase, cancel

tordieren, to twist

Torse *f.*, developable surface

totalpositiv, totally positive (*e.g. in a number field*)

Totalstetigkeit *f.*, absolute continuity

traf, *see* **treffen**

Träger *m.*, carrier, base

Trägheit *f.*, inertia

Trägheitsform *f.*, inertia form, resultant form

transponieren, to transpose

trat auf, trat ein, *etc.*, *see* **auftreten, eintreten,** *etc.*

* treffen (traf ; getroffen), to meet, strike

trennen, to separate

Trennung *f.*, distance, separation (*e.g. of variables*)

Treppenfunktion *f.*, step function

treu, true

trotz, in spite of, despite, notwithstanding

trug ab, trug auf, *etc.*, *see* **abtragen, auftragen,** *etc.*

U

über, over, above, concerning, higher than, by reason of, across, beyond, along, after, during, while, on account of, too much

über und über, over and over, out and out, through and through, completely

überall, everywhere, all over, throughout, at all times, upon the whole

überaus, exceedingly, excessively

Überblick *m.*, synopsis, survey

Überdeckung *f.*, covering

überdies, moreover, in addition, besides

überein, in accordance, conformably, alike, agreeably (to)

übereinander, one upon another

übereinanderlagern (*sep.*), to superpose, superimpose

übereinanderlegen (*sep.*), to superpose, superimpose

übereinstimmen (*sep.*), to coincide, agree, correspond

überflüssig, superfluous, excessive, unnecessary

überführen (*sep.*), to transform, take, carry (over)

Übergang *m.*, passage (to), transition

Grenzübergang *m.*, passage to the limit

* **übergreifen** (*sep.*) (**griff über** ; **übergegriffen**), to overlap

überhaupt, in general, on the whole, at all, especially

überhin, over, slightly, superficially

Überhöhung *f.*, excess (of height)

Überlägerung *f.*, covering

Überlegung *f.*, reflection, consideration, deliberation

Übermatrix *f.*, matrix whose elements are matrices

* **übernehmen** (*sep.*) (**nahm über** ; **übergenommen**), to take over

* **übernehmen** (**übernahm** ; **übernommen**), to take possession of, assume, accept

übernommen, *see* **übernehmen**

überquer, across, diagonally

Überschiebung *f.*, transvection, transvectant

überschiessend, excess, surplus

Überschlag *m.*, estimate, rough calculation, overlap

überschlagenes Polygon, star polygon

* **überschneiden** (**überschnitt** ; **überschnitten**), to cut, intersect, overlap

Überschuss *m.*, excess

überschüssig, excess, surplus

übersichtlich, clear, distinct, synoptical

übersteigend, exceeding

überstumpf, convex, re-entrant

* **übertragen** (**übertrug** ; **übertragen**), to carry over, transmit, connect, correlate, transform, transfer

Übertragungslehre *f.*, theory of connections

* **übertreffen** (**übertraf** ; **übertroffen**), to exceed, surpass

* **überwinden** (**überwand** ; **überwunden**), to overcome

überzählig, excess, surplus

üblich, usual, customary, in use

übrig, left over, remaining, superfluous, unnecessary

übrigens, moreover, in other respects, however, as for the rest, besides

Übung *f.*, use, exercise, practice, study

im Uhrzeigersinne, clockwise

um, about, past, out, ended, over, upset, around, enclosing, surrounding, round about

um . . . herum, about, around, near, towards, concerning, for, because of, by, at, alternatively with, after

um und um, all round about, on all sides, from all sides

38

umbeschrieben, *see* **umschreiben** (*sep.*)

Umdrehung *f.*, rotation, revolution

* **umfahren (umfuhr ; umfahren**), to encircle

Umfang *m.*, girth, periphery, circumference, contour, size

umfassen, to embrace, contain, comprise

umformen (*sep.*), to deform, transform, modify, change

Umgang *m.*, turn, thread (*e.g. of a helix*)

Umgebung *f.*, neighbourhood, region

umgekehrt, converse, reciprocal, inverse, vice-versa

umgeschrieben, *see* **umschreiben** (*sep.*)

Umgrenzung *f.*, boundary, limitation, restriction

umher, about, up and down, all round, here and there

umhüllen, to envelope

umkehrbar, having an inverse, reversible

umkehren (*sep.*), to reverse, invert

Umkehrung *f.*, converse, inverse, conversion, inversion

Umklappung *f.*, reflexion with respect to a line, rotation (*e.g. about the principal diagonal of a matrix*)

Umkreis *m.*, circumscribed circle

Umkugel *f.*, circumscribed sphere

Umlauf *m.*, circuit, revolution, contour, perimeter

umlegen (*sep.*), to turn (down), lay (down), surround (with)

umordnen (*sep.*), to derange, rearrange

umrechnen (*sep.*), to convert

Umriss *m.*, contour, outline

* **umschreiben** (*sep.*) (**schrieb um ; umgeschrieben** *or* **umbeschrieben**), to re-group, rearrange (*e.g. a formula*)

* **umschreiben (umschrieb; umschrieben**), to circumscribe

umsonst, to no purpose, aimlessly

Umstand *m.*, circumstance

umständlich, in detail, detailed

umwandeln (*sep.*), to transform into, convert (into)

um . . . zu, so as, in order to, to

un-, not

unausweichbar, unausweichlich, inevitable

unbedingt konvergent, absolutely convergent

unbegrenzt, unbounded, infinite

Unbestimmte *f.*, indeterminate

unbeweglich, fixed

und, and, plus

unecht, false, improper (*e.g. fraction*)

unendlich, infinite, non-terminating

unendlich klein, infinitesimal

unentbehrlich, indispensable, absolutely necessary

unfern, near, not far from

ungeachtet, disregarded, notwithstanding, although

ungefähr, about, approximately, by chance

ungerade, odd

ungerichtet, undirected, scalar

Ungleichung *f.,* inequality

ungrad(e) = ungerade

unkurzbar, in its lowest terms

unmittelbar, immediate, direct

unten, below, beneath, at the end, at the foot

   nach unten, downwards, below (*e.g. in " bounded below "*), on the left, lower

unter, under, by, amongst, during

   untere Grenze, lower bound

Unterdeterminante *f.,* minor, cofactor

Untergruppe *f.,* subgroup

unterhalb, below, at the lower end of, under

Unterklasse *f.,* subclass, lower class

Unterlage *f.,* basis

* **unterliegen (unterlag ; unterlegen),** to be subject to, satisfy, succumb to

* **unternehmen (unternahm ; unternommen),** to attempt, undertake

Unterraum *m.,* subspace

Unterschied *m.,* difference, distinction

* **unterstreichen (unterstrich ; unterstrichen),** to underline

unterstützt, supported

untersuchen, to examine, verify, prove, investigate

* **unterwerfen (unterwarf ; unterworfen),** to submit to, refer to

Unterzahl *f.,* number belonging to the lower class

unvereinbar, incompatible, inconsistent

unverkürzbar, irreducible, irredundant, minimal

unzählbar, innumerable

Ur-, original, appertaining to the source

Urbild *n.,* prototype, inverse image, antecedent, preimage

Ursache *f.,* cause

Ursprung *m.,* origin (*but not in the sense " of co-ordinates "*)

ursprünglich, original, primitive, first

Urvariabel, *f.,* original variable

V

Valenz *f.,* valence, rank (*e.g. of a tensor*), number of indices

Variationsrechnung *f.*, calculus of variations

Verabredung *f.*, convention, agreement

verallgemeinern, to generalise

veränderlich, variable

verändern, to change, alter, vary, modify

veranlassen, to cause

veranschaulichen, to represent graphically, trace, exhibit, visualise

Veranschaulichung *f.*, graphical representation, demonstration, illustration, interpretation

verästelt, ramified, branched

Verband *m.*, lattice (*algebraic*), structure

verband, *see* **verbinden**

verbessern, to correct, refine, improve

* **verbiegen (verbog ; verbogen)**, to bend, twist, deform

* **verbinden (verband ; verbunden)**, to join, connect, combine

Verbindung *f.*, combination, connection

Verbindungsstrecke *f.*, line joining

* **verbleiben (verblieb ; verblieben)**, to remain

verbog, *see* **verbiegen**

verbunden, *see* **verbinden**

verdeutlichen, to elucidate

Verdichtung *f.*, condensation, compression, reduction

verdicken, to thicken

Verdoppelung *f.*, duplication

verdrehen, to distort, twist, warp

Vereinfachung *f.*, abbreviation, simplification, reduction

Vereinigung *f.*, union, join, sum (*e.g. of sets*)

Verengung *f.*, contraction, constriction, narrowing

Verfahren *n.*, process, operation, procedure, method

Verfeinerung *f.*, refinement

verfolgen, to pursue, continue

Verfolgungskurve *f.*, curve of pursuit

* **vergleichen (verglich ; verglichen)**, to compare

vergrössern, to make larger, magnify, increase

* **verhalten** (*reflex.*) **(verhielt ; verhalten)**, to behave, be in proportion, have a certain relation to

Verhalten *n.*, behaviour

Verhältnis *n.*, ratio, relation, proportion, rate

verjüngen, to reduce, diminish, contract (*e.g. a tensor*)

verkehrt, inverse, reversed, inverted

verketten, to link, correlate, connect by a chain

Verknüpfung *f.*, combination, connection

verlagern, to transfer, shift

verlangen, to require

verlängern, to lengthen, continue, produce (*e.g. a line*)

Verlauf *m.*, course, progress, outcome, shape, behaviour

Vermehrung *f.*, increase

Verminderung *f.*, diminution

vermischt, mixed, miscellaneous

vermitteln, to arrange, adjust, adapt

vermöge, in virtue of, in pursuance of, according to, in conformity with, on the strength of

vermuten, to conjecture

vernachlässigen, to neglect

Verneinung *f.*, negation, negative, contradiction

vernünftige Funktion, well-behaved function

veröffentlichen, to publish

Verpflanzung *f.*, parallel displacement

verringern, to diminish, decrease, reduce

Verrückung *f.*, displacement, translation

versagen, to deny, refuse

versah, *see* **versehen**

verschärfen, to sharpen, take further

Verschiebung *f.*, displacement, translation, transport

verschieden, distinct, various, different

* **verschlingen** (*reflex.*) (**verschlang ; verschlungen**), to interlace, twist, link

Verschlingungszahl *f.*, linking coefficient

verschränkt, cross, crossed, interlaced

* **verschwinden** (**verschwand; verschwunden**), to vanish

* **versehen** (**versah ; versehen**), to assign, equip, provide

* **versehen** (*reflex.*), to make an error

versetzen, to permute, arrange, vary

Versiera *f.*, versiera, witch of Agnesi (*i.e. curve whose equation is* $xy^2 = a^2\{a-x\}$)

Versinnlichung *f.*, representation

verstand, *see* **verstehen**

verständlich, intelligible, clear, comprehensible

verstärken, to amplify, intensify, reinforce

* **verstehen** (**verstand ; verstanden**), to understand

versuchen, to attempt, try

vertauschen, to permute, change, exchange, interchange, commute

Buchstabenvertauschung *f.*, substitution

Verteilung *f.*, distribution, dispersion

verträglich, compatible, consistent

* **vertreten (vertrat ; vertreten)**, to represent

vervielfachen, vervielfältigen, to multiply

Vervierfachung $f.$, quadruplication

vervollständigen, to complete

verwandeln, to convert, reduce, transform, change

verwandt, related, analogous (*also see* **verwenden**)

Verwechs(e)lung $f.$, exchange, confusion

* **verweisen (verwies ; verwiesen)**, to refer (to)

* **verwenden (verwandte** *or* **verwendete ; verwandt** *or* **verwendet) zu**, to employ for, apply to

verwiesen, *see* **verweisen**

Verwindung $f.$, twisting, twisting without change of curvature

Verzahnung $f.$, tooth, notch, dovetailing

Verzeichnis $n.$, list, index

Verzerrung $f.$, distortion, deformation

verzweigen, to branch, ramify

viel, much

vieldeutig, many-valued, having many meanings

viele, many

vielfach, multiple, reiterated, often

vielfältig, multiple, varied

Vielheit $f.$, diversity, multiplicity

Vielkant $n.$, polyhedral angle

vielleicht, perhaps, maybe, perchance

vielstellig, of many digits, of many decimal places

vielwertig, many-valued

Viereck $n.$, quadrangle

Vierseit $n.$, quadrilateral

Viertel $n.$, quarter, fourth part

voll, full, complete, total, whole

vollkommen, complete, perfect

Vollkreis $m.$, circle and its interior

Vollkugel $f.$, n-disc, solid sphere

vollständig, total, complete, perfect

vollständige Hülle, completion

Vollwinkel $m.$, complete revolution, the angle 2π

* **vollziehen (vollzog ; vollzogen)**, to complete

von, by, of, from, in, on, upon, concerning

voneinander, asunder, apart, separated

vor, for, before, in front of, on account of, though, with, against, more than, since, ago

voran, before, on, onwards, at the front, first

voranschicken (*sep.*), to observe beforehand, put at the head of

voraus, in advance, previously, in preference

Voraussage *f.*, prediction

Voraussetzung *f.*, assumption, hypothesis, supposition

vorbei, along, by, past, over

Vorbemerkung *f.*, preamble, preliminary remarks

vorbereiten (*sep.*), to prepare

vorder, front, leading, first, foremost, progressive (*e.g. derivative*)

Vorgang *m.*, process, procedure, event

Vorgänger *m.*, predecessor

* **vorgeben** (*sep.*) (**gab vor**; **vorgegeben**), to assert, give an advantage, give before

vorgeschrieben, *see* **vorschreiben**

vorhanden, present, available, existent

vorher, beforehand, before, previously, in front

vorig, previous, last, preceding

* **vorkommen** (*sep.*) (**kam vor**; **vorgekommen**), to appear, outstrip, occur

vorläufig, introductory, previous, provisional

Vorlesung *f.*, lecture

vorletzt, last but one

* **vorliegen** (*sep.*) (**lag vor**; **vorgelegen**), to exist

Vorrat *m.*, range, assortment

Vorrichtung *f.*, device

vorrücken (*sep.*), to advance

* **vorschreiben** (*sep.*) (**schrieb vor**; **vorgeschrieben**), to prescribe, set, assume, instruct

Vorschrift *f.*, rule

* **vorstehen** (*sep.*) (**stand vor**; **vorgestanden**), to precede, project, direct

vorstellen (*sep.*), to represent, demonstrate, put forward

Vorstellung *f.*, idea, representation

Vorteil *m.*, advantage

  Rechenvorteil *m.*, short cut

vorüber, before, in front, along by, past, finished

vorvorletzt, last but two

vorwärts, forward, on, in front

Vorzahl *f.*, coefficient

Vorzeichen *n.*, sign

W

waag(e)recht, *see* **wag(e)recht**

* **wachsen** (**wuchs**; **gewachsen**), to grow, increase

Wachstum *n.*, growth, increase

* **wägen** (**wog**; **gewogen**), to weigh

wag(e)recht, horizontal

Wahl *f.*, choice, alternative, selection

wählen, to choose, select

wahllos, (at) random

wahr, true

während, during, whilst, although

Wahrnehmung *f.*, observation

Wahrscheinlichkeit *f.*, probability

walzenförmig, cylindrical

Wälzungs- (**winkel**), (angle) of revolution

wandern, to travel, move (*e.g. on a surface*)

wandte, *see* **wenden**, **anwenden**, *etc.*

wann, when

warf, *see* **werfen**, **aufwerfen**, *etc.*

-wärts, towards

warum, why, wherefore, on what account, for what reason

was, what, what a lot, how many, that which, whatever

was für, what kind of

Wechsel *m.*, change (over), variation

wechselseitig, mutual, reciprocal

Wechselwinkel *m.*, one of a pair of alternate angles, *e.g. A, B or C, D in figure*

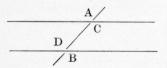

Wechselwirkung *f.*, interaction

weder, neither, than

weder . . . noch, neither . . . nor

weg-, away, off

Weg *m.*, path, route, means, way, distance

Wegegruppe *f.*, fundamental group, group of paths

wegen, because of, with regard to, in consideration of

* **wegfallen** (*sep.*) (**fiel weg**; **weggefallen**), to cancel (out), be omitted

* **wegheben** (*sep.*) (*reflex.*) (**hob weg**; **weggehoben**), to cancel (out), carry away

wegkürzen (*sep.*) (*reflex.*), to cancel out

* **wegnehmen** (*sep.*) (**nahm weg**; **weggenommen**), to deduct, subtract, take away

wegschaffen (*sep.*), to do away with, cancel, remove

* **wegstreichen** (*sep.*) (**strich weg**; **weggestrichen**), to strike off, cancel

* **wegwerfen** (*sep.*) (**warf weg**; **weggeworfen**), to throw away, reject

weil, because, since

Weise *f.*, way, manner

* **weisen** (**wies**; **gewiesen**) to point, show

weiss, *see* **wissen**

Weite *f.*, width, breadth, distance, range, amplitude

weiter, further

weiterführen, to continue, pursue further

weitläufig, weitläuftig, distant, vast, lengthy, diffused, detailed

welch, which, what

wellig, wavy, undulatory, sinuous

Wendelfläche *f.*, right helicoid, screw surface

* **wenden** (**wandte**; **gewandt**), to employ, turn

* **wenden** (*reflex.*), to turn, apply to

Wendepunkt *m.*, point of inflexion

wenig, little

wenige, few

weniger, less, minus, fewer

wenigstens, at least, at all events

wenn, if, when, in case, provided, whenever

wer, who, he who

* **werfen** (**warf**; **geworfen**), to cast, throw

* **werfen** (*reflex.*) (**warf**; **geworfen**), to become warped

Werk *n.*, work, opus

Wert *m.*, value, worth

wertgebend, significant

wesentlich, essential, real, fundamental, intrinsic, principal

wichtig, weighty, of importance

wider, against, contrary to, in opposition to, again, once more, in return

widersinnig, absurd, contradictory

Widerspruch *m.*, contradiction

Widerstand *m.*, resistance

wie, how, in what degree, as, like, for instance, as if, such as, when

wieder, again, once more, in return

wiederholt, repeated, iterated, successive

wiederkehren (*sep.*), to recur, repeat

* **wiegen** (**wog**; **gewogen**), to weigh

Willkür *f.*, arbitrariness

windschief, skew

Windung *f.*, turn, thread, torsion, convolution

Windungspunkt *m.*, branchpoint

Winkel *m.*, angle

Winkelfunktion *f.*, trigonometric function

winkelrecht, perpendicular

winkeltreu, equiangular, isogonal, angle-preserving, conformal

wirklich, actual, real, genuine, effective

Wirkung *f.*, effect

* **wissen** (**wusste; gewusst**), to know

Wissenschaft *f.*, science

wo, where, in what place, in, on, at which, that, if, in which case

wog, *see* **wiegen**

wohl, well, indeed, perhaps, probably

wohlgeordnet, well ordered

Wölbung *f.*, convexity, arch, vault

wonicht, if not, unless

Wort *n.*, word

Wortlaut *m.*, wording

wörtlich, verbatim

wuchs, *see* **wachsen**

Wulst *m.*, torus, anchor-ring

Wurf *m.*, throw, set of four elements, projection, anharmonic range or pencil

Würfel *m.*, cube, die

Würfelgitter *n.*, cubical lattice

würfeln, to cast, throw dice

Wurzel *f.*, root, radical

Wurzelausdruck *m.*, radical, surd

wusste, *see* **wissen**

Z

Zahl *f.*, number, digit

zählen, to count, number, belong to

Zahlenebene *f.*, complex plane, Gaussian plane

Zahlenlinie *f.*, number scale, real line

zahlenmässig, numerical, quantitative

Zahlenraum *m.*, space, continuum

Zahlentheorie *f.*, theory of numbers

Zähler *m.*, numerator

Zahn *m.*, tooth

Zauber *m.*, magic

Zehner *m.*, ten

Zehnerbruch *m.*, decimal fraction

Zehnerlogarithmus *m.*, logarithm to the base ten, common logarithm

Zeichen *n.*, sign, symbol, operator

zeichnen, to sign, draw, graph, trace, mark, delineate, represent

zeigen, to show, point out

Zeiger *m.*, index, pointer, arrow

Zeile *f.*, line, row

Zeit *f.*, time

Zeitabschnitt *m.*, period, interval of time

Zelle *f.*, cell

zentrisch, central

Zentrum *n.*, centre

Zerfällung *f.*, decomposition, splitting

zergliedern, to dissect, analyse

zerlegbar, decomposable, reducible, factorisable, composite

zerlegbarer Raum, space which is the union of closed, distinct sets

zerlegen, to divide up, analyse, factorise, partition, decompose, break up, separate

* **zerreissen** (**zerriss** ; **zerrissen**), to tear

zerren, to strain, deform

Zerspaltung *f.*, splitting, subdivision

Zerstückelung *f.*, fragmentation, tearing apart

* **ziehen** (**zog** ; **gezogen**), to draw, trace, extract, describe (*e.g. a circle*)

Ziel *n.*, aim, goal

ziemlich, fit, suitable, tolerable

Ziffer *f.*, cypher, character, numeral, digit

Zins *m.*, interest

Zipfel *m.*, tip, corner

Zirkel *m.*, pair of compasses

Zirkelschluss *m.*, vicious circle

zitieren, to cite, quote

zog, *see* **ziehen, abziehen,** *etc.*

Zoll *m.*, inch

Zopf *m.*, band, braid

zu, to, too, by, in, at, at the rate of, on, for, in order to

zudecken (*sep.*), to cover up, conceal

zudem, moreover, besides, in addition

zuerst, at first

zufällig, chance, accidental, random

zufolge, in consequence of, in virtue of, according to

Zug *m.*, line, path

zugänglich, accessible

zugehörig, belonging to, associated with, corresponding

zugleich, at the same time, also, together (with)

Zuglinie *f.*, tractrix

* **zulassen** (*sep.*) (**liess zu** ; **zugelassen**), to leave closed, admit, permit

zulässig, admissible *etc.* (*see* **zulassen**)

zuletzt, finally, after all

zumal, above all, particularly, especially

zumeist, mostly

zunächst, in the first instance, first of all, chiefly, next (to)

Zunahme *f.*, increase

* **zunehmen** (*sep.*) (**nahm zu** ; **zugenommen**), to increase, ascend

zuordnen (*sep.*), to associate with, correlate, relate, assign, coordinate

Zuordnung *f.*, correspondence, coordination

zurück, back, backwards, in the rear

zurückführen (*sep.*), to reduce, refer, lead back

zurückkehren (*sep.*), to return, revert

zurücklegen (*sep.*), to cover, travel, lay aside

* **zurückwerfen** (*sep.*) (**warf zurück** ; **zurückgeworfen**), to reflect

zusammen, together, jointly

zusammenfassen (*sep.*), to comprise, collect, combine, sum up, recapitulate

zusammengesetzt, composite, compound, complex

Zusammenhang *m.*, connectivity, coherence, relation

zusammenhängend, connected, coherent

zusammenhangslos, totally disconnected

* **zusammenlaufen** (*sep.*) (**lief zusammen ; zusammengelaufen**), to converge, meet in a point

* **zusammenschliessen** (*sep.*) (**schloss zusammen ; zusammengeschlossen**), to join together

zusammensetzen (*sep.*), to compose, combine

zusammenstellen (*sep.*), to collect, compile, tabulate

Zusatz *m.*, corollary, lemma

Zustand *m.*, condition, position

* **zutreffen** (*sep.*) (**traf zu ; zugetroffen**), to be valid, hold

zuvor, before, formerly, once

Zuwachs *m.*, increment, increase

zuweilen, sometimes, now and then

zuwider, contrary to, against, offensive

Zwang *m.*, constraint, restraint, force

zwar, it is true, indeed, of course, truly

Zweck *m.*, purpose, aim, end, object

zweckmässig, useful, answering the purpose, expedient, practical, suitable

Zweibein *n.*, edge of a trihedral

zweiblättrig, two-sheeted

zweideutig, two-valued, ambiguous

Zweieck *n.*, lune, figure bounded by two great circles on a sphere

Zweig *m.*, branch

zweiletzt, last but one

zweischalig, two-sheeted

zwischen, between, among, intermediate

Zykel *m.*, cycle

zyklisch, cyclic, circular

Zykloide *f.*, cycloid

zyklometrisch, inverse trigonometric, cyclometric

Zyklus *m.*, cycle

Zylinder *m.*, cylinder

Zylinderhuf *m.*, ungula of a cylinder

Abbreviations

a. = aus, from, out of

a. a. O. = am angeführten Orte, *loc. cit.*, in the place mentioned

abgk., abk. = abgekürzt, abbreviated

Abh. = Abhandlung(en), treatise(s)

Abschn. = Abschnitt, paragraph

Abt. = Abteilung, section

Akad. = Akademie, academy

allg., allgm. = allgemein, general

angew. = angewandt, applied

Anm. = Anmerkung, note

Ann. = Annalen, annals

Anz. = Anzeiger, journal, review (advertiser)

Arch. = Archiv, archives

Art. = Artikel, article

Aufl. = Auflage, edition

ausgel. = ausgelassen, omitted

b. = bei, beim, bei dem, at, with, by, near

B. = Band ; Beispiel, volume ; example

BB. = Bände, volumes

Bd. = Band, volume

Bdtg., Bed. = Bedeutung, meaning

bed. = bedeutet, signifies

Ber. = Bericht, report

bes. = besonders, especially

bez. = bezüglich, with reference to

bezw., bzw. = beziehungsweise, respectively ; and/or

Bmk., Bmkg. = Bemerkung, observation, note

bzw., *see* bezw.

darst. = darstellend, descriptive

das. = daselbst, in the same place

dass. = dasselbe, the same

dgl. = dergleichen, similarly, the like

d. h. = das heisst, *i.e.*, that is

d. i. = das ist, *i.e.*, that is

d. O. = der Obige, the above

Einl. = Einleitung, introduction

Einzelschr. = Einzelschrift, isolated issue

Erl. = Erläuterung, explanation, note

ev. = eventuell, perhaps, possibly

ff., fg., fgg. = folgende, the following

F. f. = Fortsetzung folgt, to be continued

Forts. = Fortsetzung, continuation

50

Fussn. = **Fussnote,** footnote

gek. = **gekürzt,** abbreviated

gen. = **genannt,** mentioned

Ges. = **Gesellschaft,** society

gew. = **gewöhnlich,** usually

g. g. T. = **grösster gemeinsamer Teil,** greatest common divisor

gleichbd. = **gleichbedeutend,** synonymous

Hs. = **Handschrift,** manuscript

i. allg. = **im allgemeinen,** in general

i. b. = **im besondern,** in particular

J. = **Journal,** journal

Jber. = **Jahresbericht,** annual report

Jg. = **Jahrgang,** year

K., Kap. = **Kapitel,** chapter

k. g. T. = **kleinster gemeinsamer Teil,** least common multiple

Kl. = **Klasse,** class

Math. = **Mathematik,** mathematics

math. = **mathematisch,** mathematical

m. a. W. = **mit anderen Worten,** in other words

Mitt. = **Mitteilung,** communication, information

m. s. = **man sehe,** see, compare

Nachr. = **Nachrichten,** reports, news

näml. = **nämlich,** that is to say

namtl. = **namentlich,** especially

nat., naturwiss. = **naturwissenschaftlich,** scientific

naturf. = **naturforschend,** pertaining to scientific research

Nr. = **Nummer,** number

od. = **oder,** or

o. U. d. B. = **ohne Unterschied der Bedeutung,** without difference in meaning

S. = **Seite,** page

S.-B. = **Sitzungsbericht(e),** report(s) of a meeting

Schr. = **Schriftenreihe,** series of papers

Sem. = **Seminar,** college, special class

Ser. = **Serie,** series

s. o. = **siehe oben,** see above

sog. = **sogenannt,** so-called

s. u. = **siehe unten,** see below

s. v. a. = **so viel als,** as much as

s. v. w. = **so viel wie,** as much as

tech. = **technisch,** technical

teilw. = **teilweise,** partly

u. = **und;** **unter,** and; under

u. a. = **unter anderm;** **und andere,** amongst other things; and others

u. a. a. O. = **und an andern Orten**, and elsewhere

übhpt. = **überhaupt**, in general

übtrgn. = **übertragen**, transcribed ; translated

usf. = **und so fort**, and so forth

usw. = **und so weiter**, and so on

Verh. = **Verhandlung**, discussion

verk. = **verkürzt**, abbreviated

verl. = **verlängert**, extended, lengthened

verm. = **vermehrt**, enlarged, increased

Veröff. = **Veröffentlichung**, publication

versch. = **verschieden**, different

vgl. = **vergleiche**, see, compare

viell. = **vielleicht**, perhaps

Vierteljschr. = **Vierteljahrsschrift**, quarterly issue

Wiss. = **Wissenschaft**, science, knowledge

wissensch. = **wissenschaftlich**, scientific, scholarly

w. o. = **wie oben**, as above

w. z. b. w. = **wie zu beweisen war**, Q.E.D.

Z., Zeitschr. = **Zeitschrift**, journal, periodical

ZAMP = **Zeitschrift für angewandte Mathematik und Physik**, journal for applied mathematics and physics

z. B. = **zum Beispiel**, for example, e.g.

z. d. St. = **zu der Stelle**, referring to that passage

zsgs. = **zusammengesetzt**, compound

z. T. = **zum Teil**, partly

zw. = **zwischen**, between

z. Z. = **zur Zeit**, at present, now

Grammatical Sketch

GENDER. NOMINATIVE CASE

In German all nouns are written with a capital letter.

All nouns have gender, either masculine, feminine or neuter.

There are four cases : nominative, accusative, genitive and dative.

The gender and case of a noun are shown by the determining word preceding it.

The *nominative* of the definite article, *the,* is

> **der** (*Masc.*)   **die** (*Fem.*)   **das** (*Neut.*)
>
> e.g. **der Anfang,** *the beginning*
> **die Mitte,** *the middle*
> **das Ende,** *the end*

The *nominative* of the indefinite article, *a,* is

> **ein** (*Masc.*)   **eine** (*Fem.*)   **ein** (*Neut.*)
>
> e.g. **ein Anfang,** *a beginning*
> **eine Mitte,** *a middle*
> **ein Ende,** *an end*

The third person singular personal pronouns, *he, she, it,* are

> **er, sie, es**

In German *it* may be **er, sie** or **es** according to the gender of the noun it represents. Thus **er** may mean *he* or *it* and **sie** *she* or *it.*

Wo ist der Anfang? Da ist er. *Where is the beginning ? There it is.*

Die Mitte ist schwer. Sie ist schwer. *The middle is difficult. It is difficult.*

Ist das Ende klar? Ja, es ist klar. *Is the end clear? Yes, it is clear.*

The third person plural personal pronoun, *they*, is **sie** for all genders.

e.g. **sie sind gut**, *they are good*

Vocabulary

der Anfang, *the beginning*
die Mitte, *the middle*
das Ende, *the end*
er, sie, es ist, *he, she, it is*
sie sind, *they are*
gut, *good*

klar, *clear*
schwer, *difficult, heavy*
da, *there*
ja, *yes*
wo? *where?*

SECTION II

ACCUSATIVE CASE. PRESENT TENSE OF VERB

The *accusative* of the definite article is

den (*Masc.*) **die** (*Fem.*) **das** (*Neut.*)

The *accusative* of the indefinite article is

einen (*Masc.*) **eine** (*Fem.*) **ein** (*Neut.*)

The noun has the same form in the accusative as in the nominative.

e.g. **Der Beweis hat einen Anfang, eine Mitte und ein Ende.** *The proof has a beginning, a middle and an end.*

The *accusative* of the third person singular personal pronoun is

ihn (*Masc.*) **sie** (*Fem.*) **es** (*Neut.*)

54

Present Tense of Verb

All *infinitives* of German verbs end in **–n**.

e.g. **machen,** *to make* ; **rechnen,** *to calculate* ; **sein,** *to be* ; **haben,** *to have* ; **werden,** *to become*

To find the stem of the verb remove the final **–n** or **–en** of the infinitive.

The *present tense* is formed by adding to the stem the endings : **–e, –st (–est), –t (–et), –en, –t (–et), –en, –en.**

e.g.

ich mache	*I make*	**ich rechne**	*I calculate,*
du machst	*you make*	**du rechnest**	*etc.*
er (sie, es)	*he (she, it)*	**er (sie, es)**	
macht	*makes*	**rechnet**	
wir machen	*we make*	**wir rechnen**	
ihr macht	*you make*	**ihr rechnet**	
Sie machen	*you make*	**Sie rechnen**	
sie machen	*they make*	**sie rechnen**	

Sie machen, *you make.* This form (**Sie** is always written with a capital letter) is the polite form of address.

There is only one form in German, **ich mache,** for three forms in English : *I make, I am making, I do make.*

A few verbs do not follow the above rules. These " irregular " verbs include **sein, haben** and **werden.** The *present tense* of these is :

ich bin	**ich habe**	**ich werde**
du bist	**du hast**	**du wirst**
er ist	**er hat**	**er wird**
wir sind	**wir haben**	**wir werden**
ihr seid	**ihr habt**	**ihr werdet**
Sie sind	**Sie haben**	**Sie werden**
sie sind	**sie haben**	**sie werden**

Er macht einen Fehler (er macht ihn). *He makes an error (he makes it).*

Sie beschreibt einen Kreis. *She is describing a circle.*

Wir suchen die Lösung und finden sie nicht. *We are looking for the solution and do not find it.*

Haben Sie das Buch? Nein, ich habe es nicht. *Do you have the book? No, I do not have it.*

Vocabulary

der Beweis, *the proof*	**machen,** *to make, do*
der Fehler, *the error*	**rechnen,** *to calculate, count*
der Kreis, *the circle*	**sein,** *to be*
die Lösung, *the solution*	**suchen,** *to look for*
das Buch, *the book*	**werden,** *to become*
beschreiben, *to describe*	**nein,** *no*
finden, *to find*	**nicht,** *not*
haben, *to have*	**und,** *and*

SECTION III

GENITIVE CASE. WORD-ORDER: (1) QUESTIONS. (2) CONJUNCTIONS

The *genitive* of the definite article is

des *(Masc.)*   **der** *(Fem.)*   **des** *(Neut.)*

The *genitive* of the indefinite article is

eines *(Masc.)*   **einer** *(Fem.)*   **eines** *(Neut.)*

In the *genitive case* most masculine nouns and all neuter nouns take **-s** in the singular (monosyllabic nouns often **-es**). The feminine noun is unchanged.

e.g. **des Anfangs   der Mitte   des Buches**

Word-order: (1) Questions

The verb normally occupies second place in the sentence.

e.g. **Ich habe die Lösung.** *I have the solution.*

In questions the verb is placed before the subject. (*Inverted order.*)

e.g. **Haben Sie die Lösung?**   *Do you have the solution ?*

If there is an interrogative word or phrase at the beginning, the verb follows it immediately.

Wo ist die Wurzel der Gleichung?	*Where is the root of the equation ?*
Wer hat das Buch des Lehrers?	*Who has the teacher's book ?*
Warum sagt er nichts?	*Why does he say nothing ?*
Wie machen Sie das?	*How do you do that ?*
Wie ist der Beweis? Wie schwer ist er?	*What is the proof like ? How difficult is it ?*
Was machen Sie?	*What are you doing?*
Was für eine Kunst ist es?	*What kind of an art is it ?*

Word–order: (2) Conjunctions

When a subordinating conjunction introduces a subordinate clause the verb is put to the end of the clause. (*Transposed order.*)

e.g. **weil der Anfang schwer ist,** *because the beginning is difficult.*

A subordinate clause is always separated from the principal clause by a comma.

e.g. **Er findet, dass der Anfang schwer ist.** *He finds that the beginning is difficult.*

When the subordinate clause precedes the principal clause, the verb is placed first in the principal clause. (*Inverted order.*)

e.g. **Obwohl der Anfang schwer ist, ist die Arbeit bald fertig.** *Although the beginning is difficult, the work is soon finished.*

The following are common subordinating conjunctions :

als, *as, than, when*
als ob, *as if*
bevor, ehe, *before*
bis, *till, until*
da, *as, since*
damit, *in order that*
dass, *that*
falls, *in case*

indem, während, *while*
nachdem, *after*
ob, *whether*
obgleich, obwohl, *although*
seit, seitdem, *since*
weil, *because*
wenn, *if, when*
wie, *as*

Normal word-order is found after the following conjunctions : **und**, *and* ; **aber**, *but* ; **allein**, *but* ; **denn**, *for* ; **sondern**, *but* ; **oder**, *or*.

Vocabulary

der Lehrer, *the teacher*
die Arbeit, *the work*
die Gleichung, *the equation*
die Kunst, *the art*
die Wurzel, *the root*
das ; *the* ; *that*
sagen, *to say, tell*
fertig, *finished, ready*

bald, *soon*
nichts, *nothing*
warum?, *why ?*
was?, *what ?*
was für (ein)?, *what kind of (a) ?*
wer?, *who ?*
wie?, *how ?*

SECTION IV

DATIVE CASE. PREPOSITIONS. WORD-ORDER

The *dative* of the definite article is

dem (*Masc.*)   **der** (*Fem.*)   **dem** (*Neut.*)

The *dative* of the indefinite article is

einem (*Masc.*)   **einer** (*Fem.*)   **einem** (*Neut.*)

Masculine and neuter monosyllabic nouns sometimes add **-e** in the *dative* singular. The feminine noun is unchanged.

e.g. **Wir geben dem Manne ein Beispiel.** *We give the man an example.*

The *dative* of the third person singular personal pronouns is

ihm (*Masc.*) **ihr** (*Fem.*) **ihm** (*Neut.*)

e.g. **Sie zeigt dem Lehrer das Buch. Sie zeigt es ihm.**
She is showing the book to the teacher. She is showing it to him.

Prepositions

The following prepositions always govern the *dative* :

aus, *out of, from*
ausser, *besides, except*
bei, *near, with, among*
gegenüber, *opposite*
mit, *with*

nach, *after, towards, according to*
seit, *since*
von, *of, from, by*
zu, *to, at, for*

e.g. **Das Beispiel kommt nach dem Satze.** *The example comes after the theorem.*

The following prepositions always govern the *accusative* :

durch, *through*
für, *for*
gegen, *against, towards*

ohne, *without*
um, *about, around*
wider, *against*

e.g. **Die Kurve geht durch den Punkt.** *The curve goes through the point.*

The following prepositions normally govern the *genitive* :

(an)statt, *instead of*
ausserhalb, *outside*
innerhalb, *inside*
diesseits, *on this side of*

jenseits, *on that side of*
trotz, *in spite of*
während, *during*
wegen, *because of, on account of*

e.g. **Der Punkt liegt ausserhalb des Gebiets.** *The point lies outside the domain.*

The following prepositions govern the *accusative* when they indicate motion towards (in answer to the question : Whither ?) and the *dative* when they indicate rest (in answer to the question : Where ?) :

an, *at, by the side of*	**über**, *over, above, concerning*
auf, *on, onto*	**unter**, *under, among*
hinter, *behind*	**vor**, *before*
in, *in, into*	**zwischen**, *between*
neben, *beside, near*	

e.g. **Wir verbiegen einen Kreis in eine Kurve.** *We deform a circle into a curve.*

Die Funktion ist regulär in dem Gebiet. *The function is regular in the domain.*

The preposition and the definite article are often contracted. Common contractions are :

an das = ans	**bei dem = beim**	**von dem = vom**
an dem = am	**in das = ins**	**zu der = zur**
auf das = aufs	**in dem = im**	**zu dem = zum**

Word-order

If any word other than the subject begins the principal clause the verb generally precedes the subject. (*Inverted order*—see Questions, Section III.)

e.g. (with a prepositional phrase)
Im Gebiet finden wir einen Punkt. *In the domain we find a point.*

Vocabulary

der Mann, *the man*	**geben**, *to give*
der Punkt, *the point*	**gehen**, *to go*
der Satz, *the theorem*	**kommen**, *to come*
die Funktion, *the function*	**liegen**, *to lie*
die Kurve, *the curve*	**verbiegen**, *to deform*
das Beispiel, *the example*	**zeigen**, *to show*
das Gebiet, *the domain, region*	**regulär**, *regular*

DECLENSION OF DEFINITE AND INDEFINITE ARTICLES. PRONOMINAL AND POSSESSIVE ADJECTIVES. PERSONAL, INTERROGATIVE AND INDEFINITE PRONOUNS

The *definite article* is declined as follows :

	Singular			Plural
	Masc.	*Fem.*	*Neut.*	*All Genders*
Nom.	der	die	das	die
Acc.	den	die	das	die
Gen.	des	der	des	der
Dat.	dem	der	dem	den

The following *pronominal adjectives* take the same forms as the definite article :

dieser, *this* ; **jener**, *that* ; **jeder**, *each* ; **aller**, *all* ; **mancher**, *many (a)* ; **solcher**, *such (a)* ; **welcher**, *which*.

e.g. **in jedem Kreise**, *in each circle*
    Welches Beispiel suchen Sie? *Which example are you looking for ?*

The *indefinite article* is declined as follows :

	Singular			No Plural
	Masc.	*Fem.*	*Neut.*	
Nom.	ein	eine	ein	
Acc.	einen	eine	ein	
Gen.	eines	einer	eines	
Dat.	einem	einer	einem	

The *personal pronouns* are declined as follows :

	Sing.	Pl.	Sing.	Pl.	Sing. and Pl.
Nom.	ich	wir	du	ihr	Sie
Acc.	mich	uns	dich	euch	Sie
Gen.	meiner	unser	deiner	euer	Ihrer
Dat.	mir	uns	dir	euch	Ihnen

	Singular						Plural	
Nom.	**er**	*he*	**sie**	*she*	**es**	*it*	**sie**	*they*
Acc.	**ihn**		**sie**		**es**		**sie**	
Gen.	**seiner**		**ihrer**		**seiner**		**ihrer**	
Dat.	**ihm**		**ihr**		**ihm**		**ihnen**	

The *possessive adjectives* with the corresponding personal pronouns are :

ich	*I*	**mein**	*my*	**wir**	*we*	**unser**	*our*
du	*thou*	**dein**	*thy*	**ihr**	*you*	**euer**	*your*
er	*he*	**sein**	*his*	**Sie**	*you*	**Ihr**	*your*
sie	*she*	**ihr**	*her*	**sie**	*they*	**ihr**	*their*
es	*it*	**sein**	*its*				

The *possessive adjectives* and **kein**, *not a, no,* are declined like **ein** in the singular and like **die** in the plural.

The *interrogative pronoun* **wer**, *who,* is declined as follows :

Nom.	**wer**
Acc.	**wen**
Gen.	**wessen**
Dat.	**wem**

wer, *who,* and **was**, *what,* have no special form for the plural.

e.g. **Wer sind da?** *Who are there ?*

The *indefinite pronouns* **einer**, *one, someone,* and **keiner**, *none, nobody, neither,* are declined like the masculine singular of the definite article.

e.g. **Einer von ihnen geht nicht.** *One of them is not going.*

The *indefinite pronoun* **man**, *one, someone, people,* is commonly used.

NOUNS: PLURALS. WEAK NOUNS. MIXED DECLENSION. FOREIGN NOUNS. COMPOUND NOUNS. WORD FORMATION

Plurals of nouns are formed variously in German. Each plural should be noted along with the gender of the noun.

N.B. The dative plural of every noun ends in –n.

Masculine nouns form their plural by adding –e or –er to the singular and many modify the stem vowel. (i.e. the vowel in the stem of the word changes a→ä o→ö u→ü.)

e.g. **der Anfang : die Anfänge   der Mann : die Männer**

Masculine and *neuter nouns* ending in –el, –en, –er, and diminutives ending in –chen and –lein, which are always neuter, add nothing. Some modify the stem vowel.

e.g. **der Fehler : die Fehler   das Bündel : die Bündel**

N.B. Dative plural : **in diesen Fehlern**

Most *feminine nouns* add –n or –en in the plural.

e.g. **die Kurve : die Kurven**
die Gleichung : die Gleichungen

A few feminine monosyllabic nouns modify and add –e in the plural.

e.g. **die Kunst : die Künste**

Neuter nouns add either –e or –er in the plural and many modify their stem vowel. Many neuter monosyllables add –er.

e.g. **das Buch : die Bücher   das Beispiel : die Beispiele**

Nouns in German are either *weak* or *strong*. (For a full

63

declension of strong nouns, see Section VII.) A weak noun never adds anything but **-n** or **-en**. It never modifies the stem vowel in the plural.

Model of Weak Declension
Masculine

	Sing.		Pl.
Nom.	**der Mensch,** *the human being,*		**die Menschen**
Acc.	**den Menschen**	*man*	**die Menschen**
Gen.	**des Menschen**		**der Menschen**
Dat.	**dem Menschen**		**den Menschen**

Feminine

die Kurve or **die Gleichung** (Most feminine nouns are weak.)

There are no weak neuter nouns.

A few nouns belong to the *mixed declension*, i.e. they are strong in the singular, weak in the plural.

Model of Mixed Declension

	Sing.	Pl.
Nom.	**das Ende**	**die Enden**
Acc.	**das Ende**	**die Enden**
Gen.	**des Endes**	**der Enden**
Dat.	**dem Ende**	**den Enden**

Many *foreign nouns* belong to this declension since they are most readily adapted to weak inflection in the plural. The original (foreign) form is retained in the singular and declined according to the strong declension.

	Sing.	Pl.
Nom.	**der Doktor,** *the doctor*	**die Doktoren**
Acc.	**den Doktor**	**die Doktoren**
Gen.	**des Doktors**	**der Doktoren**
Dat.	**dem Doktor**	**den Doktoren**

Similarly **das Studium,** *the study* : **die Studien**

Some foreign words retain their native plural form.

e.g. **das Faktum,** *the fact* : **die Fakta**

Word Formation

Many words in German are *compound words*. From the components of the whole the meaning of the word may often be guessed.

e.g. **der Knotenpunkt**, *the node* (**der Knoten**, *the knot*, **der Punkt**, *the point*)

    die Zeichenregel, *the rule of signs* (**das Zeichen**, *the sign*, **die Regel**, *the rule*)

N.B. A connecting letter is frequently found : **s** is common, even after feminine nouns which do not take **s** as a case-ending.

e.g. **die Teilbarkeitseigenschaft**, *the divisibility property* (**die Teilbarkeit**, *the divisibility*, **die Eigenschaft**, *the property*)

In a compound word only the last component is declined.

e.g. **die Fragestellung**, *the formulation of a question* (**die Frage**, *the question*, **die Stellung**, *the posing*)

    Plural : **die Fragestellungen**, *the problems*

Many words are formed with the aid of *prefixes*.

e.g. with the prefix **vor-**   **die Vorbemerkung**, *the preliminary remark* (**die Bemerkung**, *the remark*)

    with the prefix **zer-**   **zergliedern**, *to dissect, analyse* (**das Glied**, *the component*)

Many words are formed with the aid of *suffixes*.

Common *noun suffixes* are :

(masc. suffix) **-er**	**der Lehrer**, *the teacher* (**lehren**, *to teach*)
	der Teiler, *the divisor* (**teilen**, *to divide*)
(fem. suffix) **-heit**	**die Freiheit**, *the freedom* (**frei**, *free*)
	die Wahrheit, *the truth* (**wahr**, *true*)
(fem. suffix) **-keit**	**die Möglichkeit**, *the possibility* (**möglich**, *possible*)
	die Stetigkeit, *the continuity* (**stetig**, *continuous*)

(fem. suffix) **-schaft**	die **Eigenschaft,** *the quality, property* (**eigen,** *own*)
	die **Wissenschaft,** *science, knowledge* (**wissen,** *to know*)
(fem. suffix) **-ung**	die **Lösung,** *the solution* (**lösen,** *to solve*)
	die **Gleichung,** *the equation* (**gleich,** *equal*)
(usually neut. suffix) **-nis**	das **Ergebnis,** *the result* (**ergeben,** *to yield*)
	das **Hindernis,** *the hindrance* (**hindern,** *to hinder, prevent*)

Common *adjective suffixes* are :

-artig	**eigenartig,** *peculiar*
	keilartig, *wedge-like* (**der Keil,** *the wedge*)
-bar	**lösbar,** *soluble*
	teilbar, *divisible*
-haft	**fehlerhaft,** *faulty*
	lückenhaft, *defective, incomplete* (**die Lücke,** *the gap*)
-ig	**gleichseitig,** *equilateral* (**die Seite,** *the side*)
	zehnteilig, *of (in) ten parts* (**zehn,** *ten,* **der Teil,** *the part*)
-lich	**endlich,** *finite*
	künstlich, *artificial*

Common *adverb suffixes* are :

-wärts	**vorwärts,** *forwards*
	aufwärts, *upwards*
-weise	**teilweise,** *partially*
	ausnahmsweise, *by way of exception* (**die Ausnahme,** *the exception*)
	stufenweise, *by degrees* (**die Stufe,** *the step, degree*)

Compound Numerals, see Section VIII.

ADJECTIVES AND ADVERBS

Adjectives are not declined when used predicatively.

e.g. **Der Anfang ist schwer.** *The beginning is difficult.*

Adjectives preceding a noun agree with the noun in gender, case and number, and may be declined in three ways :

(1) after the definite article or one of the pronominal adjectives declined like the definite article (see Section V) ;

(2) after the indefinite article or one of the pronominal adjectives declined like the indefinite article (see Section V) ;

(3) independent (i.e. when they are not preceded by an article or by one of the pronominal adjectives mentioned above).

A. Adjective preceding a *Masculine* noun
der **Beweis,** *the proof* : **gut,** *good*

Sing.	1	2	3	
Nom.	der gute	ein guter	guter	**Beweis**
Acc.	den guten	einen guten	guten	**Beweis**
Gen.	des guten	eines guten	guten	**Beweises**
Dat.	dem guten	einem guten	gutem	**Beweis**

Plural	1	2 and 3	
Nom.	die guten	gute	**Beweise**
Acc.	die guten	gute	**Beweise**
Gen.	der guten	guter	**Beweise**
Dat.	den guten	guten	**Beweisen**

B. Adjective preceding a *Feminine* noun
die **Frage,** *the question* : **alt,** *old*

Sing.	1	2	3	
Nom.	die alte	eine alte	alte	**Frage**
Acc.	die alte	eine alte	alte	**Frage**
Gen.	der alten	einer alten	alter	**Frage**
Dat.	der alten	einer alten	alter	**Frage**

Plural	1	2 and 3	
Nom.	die alten	alte	Fragen
Acc.	die alten	alte	Fragen
Gen.	der alten	alter	Fragen
Dat.	den alten	alten	Fragen

C. Adjective preceding a *Neuter* noun
das Beispiel, *the example* : neu, *new*

Sing.	1	2	3	
Nom.	das neue	ein neues	neues	Beispiel
Acc.	das neue	ein neues	neues	Beispiel
Gen.	des neuen	eines neuen	neuen	Beispiels
Dat.	dem neuen	einem neuen	neuem	Beispiel

Plural	1	2 and 3	
Nom.	die neuen	neue	Beispiele
Acc.	die neuen	neue	Beispiele
Gen.	der neuen	neuer	Beispiele
Dat.	den neuen	neuen	Beispielen

Adjectival endings are important because they often show the case and gender of a noun when these are not otherwise apparent.

e.g. **ein kleiner Bogen,** *a small arc* (Nom. case of Masc. noun)
ein neues Verfahren, *a new method* (Nom. or Acc. case of Neut. noun)
der schiefe Strahl, *the oblique radius* (Nom. case of Masc. noun)
der komplexen Zahl, *of, to the complex number* (Gen. or Dat. case of Fem. noun)

Adjectives form the *comparative* by adding **-er,** and the *superlative* by adding **-st** or **-est.** Some monosyllabic adjectives modify the stem vowel.

	Comp.	Sup.
e.g. **lang,** *long*	**länger**	**der, die, das längste**
kurz, *short*	**kürzer**	**der, die, das kürzeste**

N.B. **immer länger** (lit. *always longer*), *longer and longer*

A few adjectives compare irregularly :

gross, *big*	**grösser**	**der, die, das grösste**
gut, *good*	**besser**	**der, die, das beste**
hoch, *high*	**höher**	**der, die, das höchste**
nah(e), *near*	**näher**	**der, die, das nächste**

Nouns are often formed from adjectives. The adjective is written with a capital letter to show it is a noun but is still declined like an adjective.

> e.g. **der Alte,** *the old man* ; **ein Alter,** *an old man*

The neuter adjective is sometimes used as a noun.

> e.g. **das Grösste,** *the maximum* ; **das Neue,** *that which is new* ;
> **alles Neue,** *everything new*

After **etwas,** *something*, **nichts,** *nothing*, the neuter adjective is declined as in 3.

> e.g. **nichts Neues,** *nothing new*

Adjectives from the names of towns are formed by adding **-er** to the name, which retains its capital letter. These adjectives are indeclinable.

> e.g. **in den Münchener Sitzungsberichten,** *in the Munich Proceedings*

Adjectives from proper names are often formed by adding **-sch** to the name, which retains its capital letter.

> e.g. **eine Kleinsche Flasche,** *a Klein bottle*
> **der Cauchysche Satz,** *Cauchy's theorem*

Adverbs

Nearly every uninflected adjective may be used as an adverb.

> e.g. **Der Beweis ist leicht.** *The proof is easy.*
> **Er lernt leicht.** *He learns easily.*

The *comparative* of the adverb is the same as the comparative of the adjective : **leichter.**

The *superlative* of the adverb is **am leichtesten**.

e.g. **Er lernt am leichtesten von allen.** *He learns most easily of all.*

When the superlative adverb is *absolute* it is rendered either by **aufs** plus the superlative adjective :

e.g. **Er lernt aufs leichteste.** *He learns very easily.*

or with the help of another adverb :

e.g. **Er lernt sehr leicht.** *He learns very easily.*

A few adverbs compare irregularly :

bald, *soon*	**früher, eher**	**am frühesten, am ehesten**
gern, *gladly, willingly*	**lieber**	**am liebsten**
viel, *much*	**mehr**	**am meisten**
wenig, *little*	**minder, weniger**	**am mindesten, am wenigsten**
wohl, *well*	**besser**	**am besten**

N.B. **Sein Erfolg ist bestimmt.** *His success is certain.* (Here **bestimmt** is an adjective.)

Diese Linie ist bestimmt länger als die andere. *This line is certainly (definitely) longer than the other one.* (Here **bestimmt** is an adverb modifying **länger**.)

Vocabulary

der Bogen, *the arc*	**München,** *Munich*
der Erfolg, *the success*	**lernen,** *to learn*
der Sitzungsbericht, *the report (minutes) of a meeting*	**ander,** *other, different*
der Strahl, *the ray, radius*	**bestimmt,** *certain, definite*
die Flasche, *the bottle*	**klein,** *little, small*
die Linie, *the line*	**komplex,** *complex*
die Zahl, *the number*	**leicht,** *easy, light*
das Verfahren, *the procedure, method*	**schief,** *oblique, skew*
	immer, *always*
	sehr, *very*

NUMERALS

Cardinals

With the exception of **ein** the cardinals are not declined.

1 ein, eins	11 elf	21 einundzwanzig
2 zwei	12 zwölf	25 fünfundzwanzig
3 drei	13 dreizehn	30 dreissig
4 vier	14 vierzehn	40 vierzig
5 fünf	15 fünfzehn	50 fünfzig
6 sechs	16 sechzehn	60 sechzig
7 sieben	17 siebzehn	70 siebzig
8 acht	18 achtzehn	80 achtzig
9 neun	19 neunzehn	90 neunzig
10 zehn	20 zwanzig	100 hundert

101	(ein)hundertundeins
102	(ein)hundertundzwei
300	dreihundert
1,000	tausend
1,001	(ein)tausendundeins
4,000	viertausend
1,000,000	eine Million
0	null
1955	neunzehnhundertfünfundfünfzig

N.B. **ein** becomes **eins** in counting when it stands alone or follows another number,
e.g. (ein)hundertundeins, 101.

remains **ein** when it precedes another number,
e.g. einunddreissig, 31.

is declined like the indefinite article when it precedes or refers to a noun, e.g. **eine Frage,** *one* or *a question.* **Wieviele Aufgaben haben Sie? Nur eine.** *How many exercises (problems) do you have? Only one.*

Ordinals

The ordinals are formed from the cardinals by the addition of –t from 2 to 19 and of –st from 20 upwards. They are declined as adjectives.

e.g. **der fünfte Punkt,** *the fifth point* ; **Karl der Zweite,** *Charles II* ; **zum zwanzigsten Male,** *for the twentieth time* ; **der hundertundvierte Satz,** *the hundred and fourth theorem*

Exceptions are : **der erste,** *the first* ; **der dritte,** *the third* ; **der achte,** *the eighth*

Compound Numerals

Fractions are formed by adding –tel to the ordinal, which drops its final –t. The noun formed is neuter. (The suffix –tel is a reduced form of (der) **Teil,** *part,* and –teil is still found in fractions.)

e.g. **ein Drittel,** $\frac{1}{3}$; **ein Viertel,** $\frac{1}{4}$; **sieben Achtel,** $\frac{7}{8}$

$\frac{1}{2}$ is expressed in German either by the noun **die Hälfte** or by the adjective **halb.**

e.g. **die Hälfte der Zeit,** *half of the time* ; **eine halbe Stunde,** *half an hour*

The addition of the suffix –**halb** to the ordinal gives : **drritthalb,** $2\frac{1}{2}$; **vierthalb,** $3\frac{1}{2}$; **anderthalb,** $1\frac{1}{2}$, whereas **dreieinhalb,** $3\frac{1}{2}$.

The addition of the suffix –**ens** to the ordinal gives the adverb : **erstens,** *firstly* ; **zweitens,** *secondly* ; **drittens,** *thirdly.*

The addition of the suffix –**erlei** to the cardinal gives the indeclinable adjective : **einerlei,** *of one kind* ; **zweierlei,** *of two kinds* ; **allerlei,** *of all kinds.*

72

The addition of the suffix **-fach** or **-fältig** to the cardinal gives: **einfach**, *onefold*, *single*, *simple*; **zweifach**, *twofold*; **mehrfach**, *manifold*.

The addition of the suffix **-mal** to the cardinal gives the adverb: **einmal**, *once*; **zweimal**, *twice*; **hundertmal**, *a hundred times*; **das Einmaleins**, *multiplication table*.

Vocabulary

der Teil, *the part*

die Aufgabe, *the exercise, task, problem*

die Stunde, *the hour*

die Zeit, *the time*

zum ersten Male, *for the first time*

das Mal, *the time, occasion*

nur, *only*

SECTION IX

PRONOUNS

Personal Pronouns

For declension of the personal pronouns see Section V.

The accusative and dative of the third person personal pronouns (all genders, singular and plural), when they represent things and are governed by a preposition, are replaced by: **da–** plus the preposition (**dar–** before vowels).

e.g. **dabei**, **darauf**; compare *thereby*, *thereupon*

Ich rechne auf ihn.	*I am counting upon him.*
Ich rechne darauf.	*I am counting upon it.*

N.B. These compounds may introduce a subordinate prepositional clause in German (often corresponding to the English construction with the prepositional infinitive or the gerund).

e.g. **Ich rechne darauf, dass er kommt.** *I am counting upon* { *him to come.* / *his coming.* }

Interrogative Pronouns

For declension of the interrogative pronoun **wer** see Section V.

The accusative and dative of the interrogative pronoun **was**, referring to a thing, when it is governed by a preposition, are replaced by : **wo-** plus the preposition (**wor-** before vowels).

e.g. **mit wem?** *with whom ?*   **womit?** *with what ?*

Reflexive Pronouns

The reflexive pronouns are the same as the personal pronouns except in the third person.

The accusative and dative of the third person singular and plural reflexive pronouns (all genders) are **sich.**

In the reflexive verb **sich irren**, *to be mistaken*, the reflexive pronouns are in the accusative.

In the reflexive verb **sich (etwas) überlegen**, *to think (something) over to oneself*, the reflexive pronouns are in the dative.

ich irre mich	*I am*	**ich überlege mir**	*I think over,*
du irrst dich	*mistaken,*	**du überlegst dir**	*I consider (to*
er irrt sich	*etc.*	**er überlegt sich**	*myself), etc.*
wir irren uns		**wir überlegen uns**	
ihr irrt euch		**ihr überlegt euch**	
Sie irren sich		**Sie überlegen sich**	
sie irren sich		**sie überlegen sich**	

Demonstrative Pronouns

The principal demonstrative pronouns are :

der, *that, the one*	**derselbe,** *the same*
dieser, *this, the latter*	**derjenige,** *the one, that*
jener, *that, the former*	**dergleichen,** *of that kind,*
solcher, *such*	*such, the like*

der (*Demonstrative Pronoun*) is identical with **der** (*the definite article*) except in the genitive singular and the genitive and dative plural.

| | Sing. | | Plural |
	Masc.	*Fem.*	*Neut.*	*All genders*
Gen.	**dessen**	**deren**	**dessen**	**derer, deren**
Dat.				**denen**

dieser, jener, solcher are declined like the definite article (see Section V).

derselbe, derjenige are compounds (definite article plus an adjective) and are declined in the normal fashion.

| | Sing. | | Plural |
	Masc.	*Fem.*	*Neut.*	*All genders*
	derselbe	**dieselbe**	**dasselbe**	**dieselben**

dergleichen is invariable.

Relative Pronouns

The common relative pronouns are **der** and **welcher**.

der (*Relative Pronoun*) is declined like **der** (*Demonstrative Pronoun*) except that in the genitive plural only **deren** is used.

welcher is declined like the definite article. It is not used in the genitive.

The relative pronoun agrees with its antecedent in number and gender, but takes the case appropriate to its own clause. It is never omitted.

N.B. In a relative clause the verb is placed at the end. (*Transposed order.*)

e.g. **Der Mann, dem ich das Buch gebe, ist ein Lehrer.** *The man to whom I am giving the book is a teacher.*

Die Methoden, mit denen ich arbeite, sind wohlbekannt. *The methods with which I am working are well-known.*

Der Kreis, welchen ich beschreibe, ist klein. *The circle (that) I am describing is small.*

was is used instead of the relative pronoun **das** :

(1) after a neuter adjectival noun.

e.g. **das Beste, was ich habe,** *the best that I have.*

(2) after **alles**, *all*, **nichts**, *nothing*, **vieles**, *much*, or an ordinal as **das Erste**.

e.g. **Alles, was er sagt, ist wahr.** *All he says is true.*

(3) when the relative pronoun refers to a whole phrase or sentence.

e.g. **Man vermutet, dass keine Wurzeln in dieser Halbebene existieren, was auch sehr wahrscheinlich ist.**
It is conjectured (lit. *one conjectures*) *that no roots exist in this half plane, which is indeed very probable.*

The accusative and dative of the relative pronoun referring to a thing and governed by a preposition may be replaced by : **wo- (wor-)** plus the preposition.

e.g. **Die Elemente,** $\left\{\begin{array}{l}\textbf{aus denen}\\ \textbf{woraus}\\ \textbf{aus welchen}\end{array}\right\}$ **der Körper besteht, sind 0, 1, 2, 3 und 4.**

The elements of which the field consists are 0, 1, 2, 3 and 4.

Der Beweis, $\left\{\begin{array}{l}\textbf{für den}\\ \textbf{wofür}\\ \textbf{für welchen}\end{array}\right\}$ **ich mich interessiere, ist schwer.**

The proof in which I am interested is difficult.

Vocabulary

der Körper, *the body, solid, field*
die Halbebene, *the half plane*
die Methode, *the method*
das Element, *the element*
arbeiten, *to work*
bestehen aus, *to consist of, be composed of*
existieren *to exist*

sich interessieren für, *to be interested in*
rechnen auf, *to count on*
vermuten, *to conjecture*
wahr, *true*
wahrscheinlich, *probable*
wohlbekannt, *well-known*
auch, *also, too, even, indeed*

VERBS

Verbs in German as in English are classified as *weak* or *strong*. These two conjugations are distinguished by the way in which the principal parts are formed : the principal parts are *the Infinitive, the Past Tense* and *the Past Participle*.

English *to count,* (*I count, counted, have counted*) is weak and German **rechnen** is weak.

English *to choose* (*I choose, chose, have chosen*) is strong but German **wählen** is weak.

English *to measure* is weak but German **messen** is strong.

English *to find, to go, to hold, to take* are strong and German **finden, gehen, halten, nehmen** are strong.

Present Tense

   (*a*) Weak verbs. For formation of the present tense see Section II, **ich rechne,** etc.

   (*b*) Strong verbs. The endings of the present tense are the same as for weak verbs. Certain verbs change the stem vowel in the second and third persons singular :

     (1) Strong verbs with the stem vowel **a, o, au** (e.g. **halten** and **laufen,** *to run*). The vowel may modify in the second and third persons singular, e.g. **er hält, er läuft.**

     (2) Strong verbs with the stem vowel **e** (e.g. **geben, nehmen, messen, sehen,** *to see*). The stem vowel changes to **i** or **ie** in the second and third persons singular, e.g. **er gibt, er nimmt, er misst, er sieht.**
     Exceptions are **gehen,** *to go,* **stehen,** *to stand,* **heben,** *to lift.*

   (*c*) See Section II for present tense of **sein, haben** and **werden.**

Present Participle

The present participle of all verbs is formed by adding
–d to the infinitive, e.g. **rechnend**. It is frequently used
as an adjective.

> e.g. **das laufende Jahr,** *the current year*

N.B. The infinitive and not the present participle is used for
the verbal noun, e.g. **das Rechnen,** *counting, calculating.*

Past Tense (Imperfect Tense)

(a) Weak verbs. A weak verb forms its past tense by
adding –te to the stem, e.g. **rechnete, wählte.**
The verb-endings are the same as for the present
tense except in the third person singular, e.g.
er wählte.

(b) Strong verbs. A strong verb forms its past tense
by a change of the stem vowel, e.g. **fand, ging,
hielt, nahm, mass.**
There are no endings on the first and third
persons singular.

(c) The past tense of **sein** is **war**, of **haben** is **hatte**,
of **werden** is **wurde.**

ich wählte	ich fand	ich nahm
du wähltest	du fandest	du nahmst
er wählte	er fand	er nahm
wir wählten	wir fanden	wir nahmen
ihr wähltet	ihr fandet	ihr nahmt
Sie wählten	Sie fanden	Sie nahmen
sie wählten	sie fanden	sie nahmen
ich war	ich hatte	ich wurde
du warst	du hattest	du wurdest
er war	er hatte	er wurde
wir waren	wir hatten	wir wurden
ihr wart	ihr hattet	ihr wurdet
Sie waren	Sie hatten	Sie wurden
sie waren	sie hatten	sie wurden

All other tenses are formed with auxiliary verbs. These auxiliary verbs are : **sein, haben, werden.**

Past Participle

 (*a*) Weak verbs. A weak verb forms its past participle by prefixing **ge–** and adding **–t (–et)** to the stem, e.g. **gerechnet, gewählt.**

 (*b*) Strong verbs. A strong verb forms its past participle by prefixing **ge–,** adding **–en** to the stem and usually altering the stem vowel, e.g. **gefunden, gegangen, gehalten, genommen, gemessen.**

 (*c*) The past participle of **sein** is **gewesen,** of **haben** is **gehabt,** and of **werden** is **geworden.**

 (*d*) Verbs with the foreign suffix **–ieren,** e.g. **differenzieren,** *to differentiate,* do not prefix **ge–** in the past participle, e.g. **differenziert.**

The compound tenses of most verbs are formed with the auxiliary verb **haben.** Intransitive verbs of motion, intransitive verbs denoting change of state, **sein, werden** and **bleiben,** *to remain,* form their compound tenses with the auxiliary verb **sein.**

Perfect
 ich habe gewählt, *I have chosen*   **ich habe gehabt**
Pluperfect
 ich hatte gewählt, *I had chosen*   **ich hatte gehabt**
Perfect
 ich bin gegangen, *I have gone*   **ich bin gewesen**
Pluperfect
 ich war gegangen, *I had gone*   **ich war gewesen**

N.B. Word-order :

(1) The past participle normally stands at the end of the sentence.

e.g. **Er hat ein Buch darüber geschrieben.** *He has written a book about it.*

(2) In a subordinate clause the finite verb is placed at the end of the clause.

e.g. **Obgleich wir seine Theorien nicht studiert haben, haben wir davon gehört.** *Although we have not studied his theories we have heard of them.*

Future Tense

The future tense of all verbs is formed with the present tense of **werden** plus the infinitive. The infinitive goes to the end of the sentence.

e.g. **Sie werden weitere Beispiele am Schluss finden.** *You will find further examples at the end.*

Future Perfect Tense

This is formed with the present tense of **werden** plus the perfect infinitive.

e.g. **Er wird es genommen haben.** *He will have taken it.*

Conditional Tenses

These are formed with the Subjunctive.

The Subjunctive Mood

Present Tense

The present subjunctive of the verb is formed by adding to the stem the endings : **-e, -est, -e, -en, -et, -en, -en.**

ich wähle	ich finde	ich nehme
du wählest	du findest	du nehmest
er wähle	er finde	er nehme
wir wählen	wir finden	wir nehmen
ihr wählet	ihr findet	ihr nehmet
Sie wählen	Sie finden	Sie nehmen
sie wählen	sie finden	sie nehmen
ich sei	ich habe	ich werde
du seiest	du habest	du werdest
er sei	er habe	er werde
wir seien	wir haben	wir werden
ihr seiet	ihr habet	ihr werdet
Sie seien	Sie haben	Sie werden
sie seien	sie haben	sie werden

GRAMMATICAL SKETCH

Past Tense (Imperfect Tense)

    (a) Weak verbs. The past subjunctive is exactly the same as the past indicative, e.g. **ich rechnete, ich wählte.**

    (b) Strong verbs. To the stem of the past tense of a strong verb are added the endings of the present subjunctive. The stem vowel is modified, e.g. **ich fände.**

ich wählte	ich fände	ich nähme
du wähltest	du fändest	du nähmest
er wählte	er fände	er nähme
wir wählten	wir fänden	wir nähmen
ihr wähltet	ihr fändet	ihr nähmet
Sie wählten	Sie fänden	Sie nähmen
sie wählten	sie fänden	sie nähmen
ich wäre	ich hätte	ich würde
du wärest	du hättest	du würdest
er wäre	er hätte	er würde
wir wären	wir hätten	wir würden
ihr wäret	ihr hättet	ihr würdet
Sie wären	Sie hätten	Sie würden
sie wären	sie hätten	sie würden

    The Conditional Tenses are formed with the past subjunctive of **werden.**

Present Conditional

    The present conditional of all verbs is formed with the past subjunctive of **werden** plus the present infinitive. Alternatively, the past subjunctive of the verb may be used.

e.g. **er würde nehmen** or **er nähme**	*he would take*
ich würde sein or **ich wäre**	*I should be*

Past Conditional

    The past conditional of all verbs is formed with the past subjunctive of **werden** plus the perfect infinitive.

Alternatively, the pluperfect subjunctive of the verb may be used.

e.g. **ich würde genommen haben**⎫ *I should have taken*
   or **ich hätte genommen** ⎭

    er würde gegangen sein ⎫ *he would have gone*
   or **er wäre gegangen** ⎭

The subjunctive is used :

(1) in indirect speech and questions :

e.g. **Er sagt, dass er es bewiesen habe.** *He says that he has proved it.*
    Wir fragten, ob sie gekommen wären (seien). *We asked if they had come.*

N.B   **dass** is frequently omitted in German and the verb then takes its normal place.

e.g. **Er sagt, er habe es bewiesen.** *He says he has proved it.*
    Er findet, dass die Kurve eine hyperbolische Spirale ist. *He finds (that) the curve is a hyperbolic spiral.*
  or **Er findet, die Kurve ist eine hyperbolische Spirale.** *He finds (that) the curve is a hyperbolic spiral.*

(2) frequently in conditional sentences :

e.g. **Wenn die Funktionen einwertig wären, würden wir die Gleichung lösen.** *If the functions were single-valued we should solve the equation.*

    Wenn wir Mathematik studiert hätten, so hätten wir die Gleichung gelöst. *If we had studied mathematics we should have solved the equation.*

Wenn, however, may be omitted and inverted order is then used :

e.g. **Wären die Funktionen einwertig, so würden wir die Gleichung lösen.** *If the functions were single-valued we should solve the equation.*

    Hätten wir Mathematik studiert, so hätten wir usw. *If we had studied mathematics we should have etc.*

(3) after **als ob,** *as if* :

e.g. **Wir werden die Funktion integrieren, als ob sie
beschränkt wäre (sei).** *We shall integrate the function
as if it were bounded.*

(4) as the third person imperative :

e.g. **Es sei τ eine Kurve.**   *Let τ be a curve.*
   Man vergleiche.   *Compare.*

The usual forms of the imperative are :

rechne ! (familiar Sing.), **rechnet !** (familiar Plural),
calculate
rechnen Sie ! (formal Sing. and Pl.), *calculate*

The Passive Voice

The passive is formed in German with the auxiliary verb
werden (the English passive is formed with the verb *to be*)
plus the past participle of the verb.

e.g. Passive Present Infinitive **gewählt werden,** *to be chosen*

N.B. The past participle of **werden** (normally **geworden**) is
worden when it helps to form the passive.

e.g. Passive Perfect Infinitive **gewählt worden sein,** *to have
been chosen*

Passive

Present	**ein Beispiel wird gewählt**	*an example is chosen*
Past	**ein Beispiel wurde gewählt**	*an example was chosen*
Perfect	**ein Beispiel ist gewählt worden**	*an example has been chosen*
Pluperfect	**ein Beispiel war gewählt worden**	*an example had been chosen*
Future	**ein Beispiel wird gewählt werden**	*an example will be chosen*

| *Future Perfect* | ein Beispiel wird gewählt worden sein | *an example will have been chosen* |

N.B. Word order :

  The past participle goes to the end of the sentence.

In German the passive is often rendered by an active construction :

e.g. (1) by a reflexive verb. **Es wird sich zeigen.** *It will be shown.*

  (2) by using **man**, *one*. **Man hat ein Beispiel gewählt.** *An example has been chosen.*

  (3) by using **lassen**, *to let, allow, cause to have something done*, reflexively with a dependent infinitive. **Sie lassen sich leicht teilen.** *They are easily divided.*

Inseparable and Separable Verbs

Many German verbs are compounded with prefixes.

  (1) *Inseparable prefixes.* These prefixes are unaccented and do not have separate existence from the verb. The following are always inseparable :

  be-, ent-, emp-, er-, ge-, ver-, zer-
  and usually **miss-, wider-**

e.g. from **schreiben**, *to write*, **beschreiben**, *to describe*
  from **decken**, *to cover*, **entdecken**, *to discover*

Verbs compounded with these prefixes do not take the prefix **ge-** in the past participle.

e.g. **beschreiben**, (past participle) **beschrieben**

  (2) *Separable prefixes.* These prefixes are accented and are often adverbs or prepositions. Simple verbs compounded with these prefixes take on a more exact or specialised meaning.

e.g. from **nehmen**, *to take*, **abnehmen**, *to decrease*
  annehmen, *to accept, assume*
  zunehmen, *to increase*

In the present and past tenses, the prefix is separated from the verb and put last in the clause or sentence.

e.g. **Die Reihe nimmt nach dem dritten Gliede ab.** *The series decreases after the third term.*

In a subordinate clause with transposed word-order the prefix is not separated from the verb.

e.g. **Ich integrierte die Funktion, weil ich annahm, dass sie beschränkt sei.** *I integrated the function because I assumed that it was bounded.*

In the past participle the prefix **ge-** is inserted between the prefix and the verb : **angenommen, ausgewählt (auswählen,** *to select*).

Similarly **zu** is inserted when used with the infinitive.

e.g. **Es bleibt noch festzustellen, dass. . . .** *It still remains to establish that. . . .*

Inseparable prefix
   Er ist gekommen, um die Arbeit zu beginnen.
Separable prefix
   Er ist gekommen, um die Arbeit anzufangen.

He has come in order to begin the work.

N.B. In translating it is important to note separable prefixes if the text is to be understood fully.

    (3) *Inseparable or Separable prefixes.* Certain prefixes are inseparable or separable according to their accent and meaning. These prefixes are :

durch-, hinter-, über-, um-, unter-, voll-, wieder-

The prefix is inseparable when the verb is accented. The inseparable verb generally takes on a figurative meaning, e.g. **wiederholen,** *to repeat.* The prefix is separable when the prefix is accented. The separable verb generally has a literal meaning, e.g. wiederholen, *to fetch back* (holen, *to fetch*, wieder, *again*).

e.g. **Er wiederholte seine Antwort.** *He repeated his answer.*
Er holte seine Bücher wieder. *He fetched his books back.*

Modal Verbs

There are six auxiliary verbs of mood :

dürfen, (*may*), *be allowed to*   **müssen,** (*must*), *have to, be obliged to*

können, (*can*), *be able to*   **sollen,** (*shall*), *be (bound) to*

mögen, (*may*), *like to*   **wollen,** (*will*), *want to*

Present Tense

ich darf	ich kann	ich mag
du darfst	du kannst	du magst
er darf	er kann	er mag
wir dürfen	wir können	wir mögen
ihr dürft	ihr könnt	ihr mögt
Sie dürfen	Sie können	Sie mögen
sie dürfen	sie können	sie mögen
ich muss	ich soll	ich will
du musst	du sollst	du willst
er muss	er soll	er will
wir müssen	wir sollen	wir wollen
ihr müsst	ihr sollt	ihr wollt
Sie müssen	Sie sollen	Sie wollen
sie müssen	sie sollen	sie wollen

Present Subjunctive

ich dürfe	ich könne	ich möge
ich müsse	ich solle	ich wolle

Past Tense (Imperfect Tense)

ich durfte	ich konnte	ich mochte
ich musste	ich sollte	ich wollte

Past Subjunctive

ich dürfte	ich könnte	ich möchte
ich müsste	ich sollte	ich wollte

Past Participle

gedurft	gekonnt	gemocht
gemusst	gesollt	gewollt

The modal verbs are conjugated with **haben**.
They are followed by the infinitive without **zu**.

e.g. **Wir wollen folgendes beweisen.** *We want to prove the following.*

When the modal verbs are used with a dependent infinitive the form of the past participle is exactly the same as the infinitive. This rule applies also to **sehen** and **lassen**.

e.g. **Ich habe es tun können.** *I have been able to do it.*
     Er hatte es feststellen wollen. *He had wanted to establish it.*

Vocabulary

der Schluss, *the end, conclusion*
die Antwort, *the answer*
die Mathematik, *mathematics*
die Reihe, *the series*
die Spirale, *the spiral*
die Theorie, *the theory*
das Glied, *the term*
das Jahr, *the year*
beschränkt, *bounded*

einwertig, *single-valued*
hyperbolisch, *hyperbolic*
weiter, *further* (comp. of **weit,** *far*)
usw. = und so weiter, *etc., and so on*
noch, *still, yet*
ob, *if, whether*
um . . . zu with infinitive, *in order to*

Weak Verbs

Infinitive	Past Tense	Past Participle	
differenzieren	differenzierte	differenziert	*to differentiate*
feststellen	stellte fest	festgestellt	*to establish*
folgen	folgte	gefolgt	*to follow*
fragen	fragte	gefragt	*to ask*
hören	hörte	gehört	*to hear*
integrieren	integrierte	integriert	*to integrate*
lösen	löste	gelöst	*to solve*

GERMAN MATHEMATICAL VOCABULARY

rechnen	rechnete	gerechnet	*to calculate, count*
sagen	sagte	gesagt	*to say, tell*
studieren	studierte	studiert	*to study*
teilen	teilte	geteilt	*to divide*
wählen	wählte	gewählt	*to choose*
wiederholen	holte wieder	wiedergeholt	*to fetch back*
wiederholen	wiederholte	wiederholt	*to repeat*
zeigen	zeigte	gezeigt	*to show*

Strong and Irregular Verbs

Infinitive	Past Tense	Past Participle	
anfangen	fing an	angefangen	*to begin*
beginnen	begann	begonnen	*to begin*
beweisen	bewies	bewiesen	*to prove*
bleiben	blieb	geblieben	*to remain*
finden	fand	gefunden	*to find*
geben	gab	gegeben	*to give*
gehen	ging	gegangen	*to go*
haben	hatte	gehabt	*to have*
halten	hielt	gehalten	*to hold*
heben	hob	gehoben	*to lift*
kommen	kam	gekommen	*to come*
lassen	liess	gelassen	*to let*
laufen	lief	gelaufen	*to run*
messen	mass	gemessen	*to measure*
nehmen	nahm	genommen	*to take*
schreiben	schrieb	geschrieben	*to write*
sehen	sah	gesehen	*to see*
sein	war	gewesen	*to be*
stehen	stand	gestanden	*to stand*
tun	tat	getan	*to do*
vergleichen	verglich	verglichen	*to compare*
werden	wurde	geworden	*to become*

Translation

An extract from *Integration* by R. P. Gillespie

The expression for the area, $\int_a^b f(x)dx$, is called a **definite integral,** and a, b are called the **limits of integration.** It should be noted that the symbol $\int f(x)dx$ is *one* symbol.

If $f(x)$ is negative the curve $y = f(x)$ lies below the x-axis, and the curve $y = -f(x)$ lying above the x-axis is the reflection of the curve $y = f(x)$ in the x-axis. Now by the above discussion the area between the curve $y = -f(x)$ and the lines $x = a$, $x = b$, $y = 0$ is given by

$$\int_a^b [-f(x)]dx = F(a) - F(b) = -\int_a^b f(x)dx.$$

Thus when $f(x)$ is negative the formula for the area between the curve $y = f(x)$ and the x-axis, $\int_a^b f(x)dx$, gives the correct numerical value for the area but with a negative sign. If we make the convention that areas under the x-axis have negative sign, the area between the curve $y = f(x)$ and the x-axis is always given by $\int_a^b f(x)dx$.

Example 1. To find the area of a circle of radius a.

The area of the first quadrant of the circle $x^2 + y^2 = a^2$ is given by $\int_0^a \sqrt{(a^2 - x^2)}dx$. Thus the problem is to find a function whose derivative is $\sqrt{(a^2 - x^2)}$. We shall show later that such a function is $F(x) \equiv \dfrac{x}{2}\sqrt{(a^2 - x^2)} + \dfrac{a^2}{2}\sin^{-1}\left(\dfrac{x}{a}\right)$;

hence $\int_0^a \sqrt{(a^2 - x^2)}dx = F(a) - F(0) = \dfrac{a^2}{2}\sin^{-1} 1 = \dfrac{\pi a^2}{4}$.

Thus the area of the circle is πa^2.

Ein Auszug aus *Integralrechnung* **von R. P. Gillespie**

Der Ausdruck für die Fläche, $\int_a^b f(x)dx$, heisst **bestimmtes Integral** und a und b sind die **Integrationsgrenzen**. Man präge sich ein, dass der Ausdruck $\int f(x)dx$ ein *einziges* Symbol ist.

Falls $f(x)$ negativ ist, liegt die Kurve $y = f(x)$ unterhalb der x-Achse und die oberhalb der x-Achse gelegene Kurve $y = -f(x)$ ist das Spiegelbild der Kurve $y = f(x)$ an der x-Achse. Nach dem Obigen ist der Inhalt der Fläche, die von der Kurve $y = -f(x)$ und den Geraden $x = a$, $x = b$ und $y = 0$ begrenzt wird, gegeben durch

$$\int_a^b [-f(x)]dx = F(a) - F(b) = -\int_a^b f(x)dx.$$

Wenn also $f(x)$ negativ ist, dann gibt $\int_a^b f(x)dx$, den Wert des Inhalts der zwischen der Kurve $y = f(x)$ und der x-Achse liegenden Fläche, aber mit negativem Vorzeichen. Wenn wir nun festsetzen, dass unterhalb der x-Achse liegende Flächen negatives Vorzeichen haben sollen, dann ist der Inhalt der zwischen der Kurve $f(x)$ und der x-Achse liegenden Fläche immer gegeben durch $\int_a^b f(x)dx$.

Beispiele 1. Gesucht der Flächeninhalt eines Kreises vom Radius a.

Der Inhalt des 1. Quadranten des Kreises $x^2 + y^2 = a^2$ ist gegeben durch $\int_0^a \sqrt{(a^2 - x^2)}dx$. Das Problem lautet also eine Funktion zu finden, deren Ableitung $\sqrt{(a^2 - x^2)}$ ist. Wir werden später zeigen, dass $F(x) \equiv \frac{x}{2}\sqrt{(a^2 - x^2)} + \frac{a^2}{2} \arcsin \frac{x}{a}$ eine solche Funktion ist ; somit wird

$$\int_0^a \sqrt{(a^2 - x^2)}dx = F(a) - F(0) = \frac{a^2}{2} \arcsin 1 = \frac{\pi a^2}{4}.$$

Der Inhalt des Vollkreises ist dann πa^2.

An extract from *Integration of Ordinary Differential Equations* **by E. L. Ince (1943 edition)**

We consider a linear equation of the second order

$$\frac{d^2y}{dx^2} = p(x)\frac{dy}{dx} + q(x)y \quad . \quad . \quad . \quad . \quad (52{\cdot}1)$$

in which we shall regard x as a complex variable.

This type includes many equations of very great importance which cannot be solved in terms of simple combinations of elementary functions. Given such an equation, the usual procedure is to express the solution (which may be a solution satisfying certain initial conditions) in the form of an infinite series from which tables of the value of the solution may, if desired, be computed. Thus the convergence of the series is important, not only as a basis of the validity of the process, but also as an indication of the practical value of the result, for a slowly converging series is of little use to a computer.

It will be assumed that the coefficients $p(x)$, $q(x)$ are one-valued, and have derivatives of all orders except possibly for certain isolated values of x. Let $x = a$ be a value for which p, q and all derivatives are finite : we shall obtain a solution such that y and y' have assigned finite values y_0, y_0' when $x = a$.

By substituting in (52·1) we obtain the corresponding value of the second derivative, namely $y_0'' = p(a)y_0' + q(a)y_0$. Differentiating (52·1), we obtain

$$y''' = p(x)y'' + \{p'(x) + q(x)\}y' + q'(x)y,$$

and as y_0, y_0', y_0'' are known, y_0''' can be obtained immediately. Continuing the process, we obtain the values of successive derivatives for $x = a$, and thus we have the coefficients in the Taylor series

$$y = y_0 + y_0'(x-a) + y_0''\frac{(x-a)^2}{2!} + \ldots + y_0^{(n)}\frac{(x-a)^n}{n!} + \ldots.$$

Ein Auszug aus *Die Integration gewöhnlicher Differentialgleichungen* **von E. L. Ince**

Wir betrachten eine lineare Differentialgleichung zweiter Ordnung $\dfrac{d^2y}{dx^2} = p(x)\dfrac{dy}{dx} + q(x)y$ . . . . (52·1)

worin x eine komplexe Variable sei.

In diese Kategorie fallen viele sehr wichtige Gleichungen, welche nicht durch einfache Kombinationen elementarer Funktionen lösbar sind. Bei einer solchen Gleichung gibt man im allgemeinen die Lösung (welche eventuell gewissen Anfangsbedingungen genügt) in Form einer unendlichen Reihe an und errechnet daraus nötigenfalls Wertetabellen für die Lösung. Die Konvergenz der Reihe spielt somit eine wichtige Rolle, nicht nur weil die Gültigkeit der Lösungsmethode darauf beruht, sondern auch weil sie einen Hinweis auf den praktischen Wert des Resultates gibt, denn eine langsam konvergierende Reihe eignet sich schlecht zur Berechnung.

Im folgenden wollen wir annehmen, die Koeffizienten $p(x)$ und $q(x)$ seien eindeutig und, ausser eventuell für gewisse isolierte Werte von x, beliebig oft differenzierbar. a bezeichne einen Wert von x, für welchen $p(x)$, $q(x)$ und alle Ableitungen endlich sind. Wir suchen eine Lösung der Differentialgleichung, so dass y und y' an der Stelle $x = a$ vorgegebene endliche Werte y_0, y_0' annehmen.

Durch Einsetzen in (52·1) ergibt sich der entsprechende Wert der zweiten Ableitung, nämlich $y_0'' = p(a)y_0' + q(a)y_0$. Differentiation von (52·1) führt auf

$$y''' = p(x)y'' + \{p'(x) + q(x)\}y' + q'(x)y,$$

und da y_0, y_0', y_0'' bekannt sind, gewinnt man daraus y_0'''. Nacheinander erhält man so die Werte aufeinander folgender Ableitungen von y an der Stelle $x = a$ und damit die Koeffizienten der Taylorschen Reihe

$$y = y_0 + y_0'(x-a) + y_0''\frac{(x-a)^2}{2!} + \ldots + y_0^{(n)}\frac{(x-a)^n}{n!} + \ldots$$

Roman Type		German Type		German Script	
A	a	𝕬	a	*A*	*a*
B	b	𝕭	b	*B*	*b*
C	c	𝕮	c	*C*	*c*
D	d	𝕯	d	*D*	*d*
E	e	𝕰	e	*E*	*e*
F	f	𝕱	f	*F*	*f*
G	g	𝕲	g	*G*	*g*
H	h	𝕳	h	*H*	*h*
I	i	𝕴	i	*I*	*i*
J	j	𝕵	j	*J*	*j*
K	k	𝕶	k	*K*	*k*
L	l	𝕷	l	*L*	*l*
M	m	𝕸	m	*M*	*m*
N	n	𝕹	n	*N*	*n*
O	o	𝕺	o	*O*	*o*
P	p	𝕻	p	*P*	*p*
Q	q	𝕼	q	*Q*	*q*

Roman Type		German Type		German Script	
R	r	ℜ	r		
S	s, ß	S	ſ, s, ß		
T	t	T	t		
U	u	U	u		
V	v	V	v		
W	w	W	w		
X	x	X	ç		
Y	y	Y	ý		
Z	z	Z	ʒ		

MODIFIED VOWELS

Ä	ä	A	ä		
Ö	ö	Ö	ö		
Ü	ü	U	ü		
Äu	äu	Au	äu		

Modification of a vowel used to be shown by a following e, and this form is still found with capital letters, thus

$$Ae = Ä \qquad Oe = Ö \qquad Ue = Ü$$

PRINTED IN GREAT BRITAIN BY
OLIVER AND BOYD LTD
EDINBURGH